Unstressed vowels

Some words contain vowels that are difficult to hear when you say th[...]

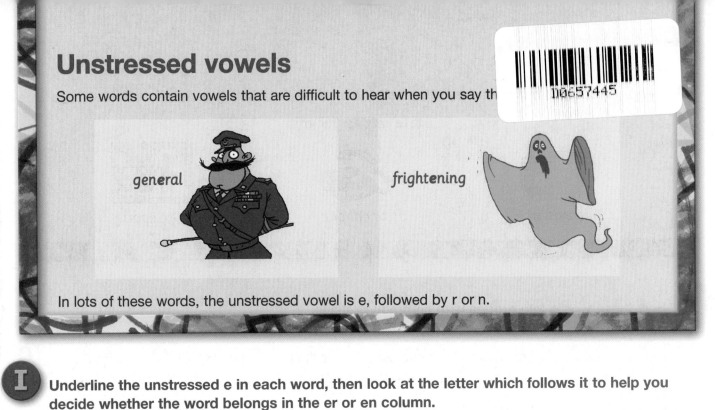

general

frightening

In lots of these words, the unstressed vowel is e, followed by r or n.

I **Underline the unstressed e in each word, then look at the letter which follows it to help you decide whether the word belongs in the er or en column.**

a interest

b desperate

c generally

d widening

e generous

f deafening

g offering

h literature

er	en
_____	_____
_____	_____
_____	_____
_____	_____
_____	_____
_____	_____

II **Sort these words into groups depending on the unstressed vowel each contains.**

a stationary

b factory

c jewellery

d stationery

e reference

f category

g conference

h boundary

i difference

j lottery

k history

l voluntary

ary	ory
_____	_____
_____	_____

ery	erence
_____	_____
_____	_____
_____	_____

Spelling clues

Shared word roots, prefixes and suffixes can help us to spell whole groups of words.

tele means 'far off'

television

telephone

teleport

I Sort these words into groups with common prefixes.

reply	preview	audible	prime	transport	primate
transplant	primary	reconsider	prevent	audience	
repeat	transfer	audition	prehistoric		

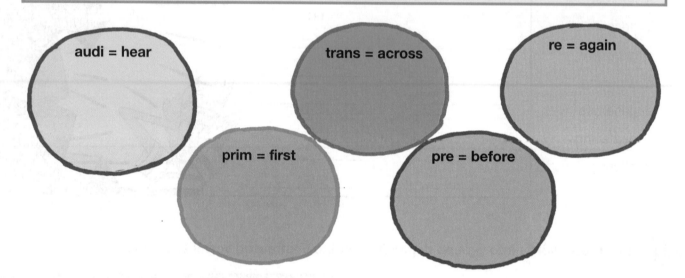

audi = hear

trans = across

re = again

prim = first

pre = before

II Choose a suffix in bold from the box to complete these word sums.

scope = look	**clude** = shut	**port** = carry

a peri + _____ = _____

b se + _____ = _____

c trans + _____ = _____

d tele + _____ = _____

e in + _____ = _____

f micro + _____ = _____

g im + _____ = _____

h con + _____ = _____

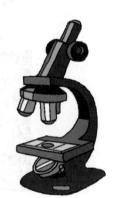

Connectives

Connectives are words or phrases used to extend sentences or join two sentences together.

Some are single words.

> We ran fast **so** we wouldn't be late.

Some are compound words.

> We visit our friends **whenever** we have time.

Some are phrases.

> We played hockey **in spite of** the rain.

Pick a word from the box to complete each compound connective. Then write the whole word at the end.

standing	over	ever	while	more	as	forward	less

a when + _____ = _____

b mean + _____ = _____

c more + _____ = _____

d where + _____ = _____

e further + _____ = _____

f none + the + _____ = _____

g not + with + _____ = _____

h hence + _____ = _____

Draw lines to match up the pairs of connective words and phrases with similar meanings.

a in addition to   as a result

b in spite of   at the same time

c consequently   another thing

d meanwhile   as well as

e henceforth   in order that

f whenever   despite

g so that   every time

h furthermore   from now on

Our changing language

Words and expressions change over time.

Some words and phrases have been replaced by more modern ones.

whenas   has become   *whenever*

 Draw lines to match up these old-fashioned words with their modern meanings.

a tarry   look at

b hark   here

c behold   there

d verily   listen to

e yonder   from where

f whence   stay

g hither   you

h thee   truly

 Write down the modern meanings of these old-fashioned words.

a nigh _____

b foe _____

c beauteous _____

d saith _____

e ye _____

f whereto _____

g prithee _____

h begone _____

Conventional English

All sentences contain a noun or pronoun, and a verb.

If the noun or pronoun is singular, you must use the singular verb form.

If the noun or pronoun is plural, you must use the plural verb form.

The girl **runs** home.

The boys **play** football.

I Complete the chart by filling in the missing singular and plural verbs.

	singular nouns			plural nouns	
a	I	run	They	_____	
b	She	tries	We	_____	
c	The man	sings	The men	_____	
d	The girl	swims	The girls	_____	
e	The bird	_____	The birds	fly	
f	He	_____	They	wash	
g	The boy	_____	The boys	sleep	
h	The child	_____	The children	play	

II Circle the correct noun in bold to complete each sentence.

a The **teacher teachers** marks the books.

b The **cat cats** chase the mouse.

c The **boy boys** reads the book.

d The **horses horse** eat the grass.

e My **brother brothers** plays football.

f The **girls girl** walk home from school.

g The **train trains** were late.

h The **shop shops** was shut.

Active and passive verbs

Verbs can be active or passive.

John **ate** the cake.

This verb is **active**.
It describes John's action.

The cake **was eaten** by John.

This verb is **passive**. It describes what happens to the cake.

Passive sentences often sound clumsy, unless some of the information is missed out of the sentence.

The window **was broken**.

This sentence creates suspense, because we don't know how the window was broken.

I Tick the box that correctly describes each sentence.

		active	passive
a	The wind blew my hat off.	☐	☐
b	I lost the key on the way home.	☐	☐
c	Our house was broken into.	☐	☐
d	The letter was written by Max.	☐	☐
e	Dad drove us to school.	☐	☐
f	My hair was trimmed by the barber.	☐	☐
g	Millie kicked the ball.	☐	☐
h	Arjan broke the window.	☐	☐
i	The garden was covered by the snow.	☐	☐
j	The candle was blown out by the draught.	☐	☐

II Write these passive sentences again, using active verbs.

a The mouse was chased by the cat. _____

b My clothes were soaked by the rain. _____

c The missing book was found by Sam. _____

d The door was opened by Jo. _____

e My magazine was delivered by the paperboy. _____

f Our test papers were marked by the teacher. _____

Clauses in complex sentences

A clause is a group of words that describe an event or situation.

Complex sentences contain more than one clause. They often contain a **main clause** and a **subordinate clause**.

The **main clause** makes sense on its own. The **subordinate clause** adds extra information, but would not make sense on its own.

It was cold so I wore a coat.

main clause   subordinate clause

 Underline the main clause in these sentences.

a Who is that, knocking at the door?

b I felt ill, so I went to bed.

c We went swimming in the river.

d It was dark when we got home.

e We went to Italy for our holiday.

f I broke the vase when I was dusting.

g Mum made me a cake for my birthday.

h The car broke down, because it had run out of petrol.

i Gran went shopping to buy some slippers.

j I drew a picture to hang on the wall.

Write a suitable subordinate clause to complete these complex sentences.

a I tidied my room so that _____.

b We went shopping for _____.

c The dog barked, because _____.

d It was a hot day, so _____.

e I picked some flowers _____.

f We posted the letter to _____.

g They kept running until _____.

h I lost my bag when _____.

i The bus was full, so _____.

j I peeled the potatoes _____.

Woof!

Brackets

We can use brackets to add extra useful information to a sentence. Brackets don't disrupt the meaning of the sentence, so you can take them out of a sentence without changing its meaning.

The monster's bad breath **(and smelly feet)** meant he had no friends.

I Choose a sensible phrase from the box to complete each sentence.

but before tea	kicked by Paul	and freezing wind
which he cut himself	a ham sandwich	a tabby

a The cat (_____) curled up and went to sleep.

b The packed lunch (_____) was delicious.

c After school (_____) we played in the park.

d The cold rain (_____) kept us indoors.

e My little brother's hair (_____) looks dreadful.

f The football (_____) flew over the fence.

II Rewrite these sentences, adding the brackets in a sensible place.

a My best friend is called Lily. (who is ten)

_____

b The old dog was dirty. (and smelly)

_____

c Pink is my favourite colour. (but not pale pink)

_____

d My new coat is really warm. (bought yesterday)

_____

e My new school is really big. (where I'm going in September)

_____

f The school holiday is going to be great. (which starts next week)

_____

Personification

Personification is where a writer describes something using words we would normally use to describe a person.

The wind **sighed** in the trees.

Love is **blind**.

Underline the personification in this passage of writing.

We sat by the ruined cottage to have our picnic. The sun smiled down on us, and birds chattered in the trees. All around us, buttercups danced in the breeze, and the nodding branches of a willow tree sheltered us from the fierce sun. The broken windows of the deserted cottage stared silently towards the sleeping hills in the distance, and the wind whispered secrets through the empty rooms.

Use personification to write descriptions of these things.

a a stream trickling over stones

_____

b an owl hooting

_____

c a rusty gate squeaking

_____

d storm clouds gathering

_____

e stars twinkling

_____

f bees humming

_____

Biography and autobiography

It can be very interesting to read about the lives of famous or interesting people.

An **autobiography** is the life story of a person, written by that person. Autobiographies tend to be written in the first person.

> I was born in Dublin in 1908.

A **biography** is also a life story, but it is written by somebody else. Biographies are written in the third person.

> She was born in Dublin in 1908.

I Tick whether each sentence comes from a biography or an autobiography.

biography   autobiography

a He was a fair and popular king, who brought peace and prosperity to his subjects.

b I left school at the age of 14 and went to work in a milliner's shop.

c My father was in the army so we moved around a lot.

d Her acting career began at the age of seven, when she appeared in a TV commercial.

e We lived in a street of small, terraced houses, each with a small back yard.

f She worked tirelessly to develop the vaccine.

II This is a short extract from the autobiography of a fictional sportswoman. Rewrite it as a biography.

> When I was eight, I was sent to a strict girls' boarding school. I missed my family terribly and never settled into school life, so I was thrilled when the war came and I was evacuated to Wales with my three brothers. For the next four years we lived on a farm, so it was a dreadful shock to return to post-war London, and to school.

Proverbs

Proverbs are **wise sayings**. They are often very old, but most of them are still true!

Too many cooks spoil the broth.

I **Complete these proverbs.**

a The grass is always greener _____.

b The early bird _____.

c A bird in the hand is worth _____.

d Great minds _____.

e Every cloud _____.

f A bad workman _____.

g Many a true word is _____.

h Let sleeping dogs _____.

II **Write down what you think each of these proverbs means.**

a Many hands make light work.

_____

b Don't put all your eggs in one basket.

_____

c Two heads are better than one.

_____

d A stitch in time saves nine.

_____

e Out of the frying pan, into the fire.

_____

f Don't count your chickens before they hatch.

_____

g Look before you leap.

_____

Adverbs

Adverbs **describe verbs**. They can tell us the following things:

How – for example, *slowly, quickly*

When – for example, *now, soon, later*

Where – for example, *here, outside*

How often – for example, *rarely, never*

Circle the adverb in each sentence.

a Jamie slipped silently out of the door.

b Jo ran outside.

c We ate quickly so we could go and play.

d You never do your homework.

e We'll make it later.

f Dad left the shopping there.

g The tortoise crawled slowly down the garden.

h Mum shouted angrily.

i Sam skated unsteadily on the slippery floor.

j I always save my pocket money.

II **Pick a sensible adverb from the box to complete each sentence.**

soon	nearly	here	soundly	quickly	happily	always	brightly

a Joshua sprinted _____ home.

b Bring the book _____.

c The stars twinkled _____ in the sky.

d We _____ have fish and chips on Friday.

e I've _____ finished my book.

f The little girl smiled _____.

g The baby slept _____.

h My friend will be here _____.

Spelling rules

Learning spelling rules can help us to spell whole families of words.

Using a spelling rule can help us to add a suffix to words that end in a consonant then y.

You can usually add the suffixes ing, and ly, without changing the spelling of the base word.

With ness, er, est, ed, and sometimes ly, you need to change the final y of the base word to **i** before you add the suffix.

fly + ing = flying

greedy + ness = greediness

I Complete these word sums using the rules above.

a empty + ness = _____

b fry + ing = _____

c deny + ed = _____

d ready + ly = _____

e sleepy + ly = _____

f windy + er = _____

g silly + ness = _____

h carry + ing = _____

i friend + ly = _____

II Choose the correct spelling from the words in bold to complete each sentence.

a The cat stretched _____. **lazyly   lazily**

b The lion looked _____ at us. **hungrily   hungryly**

c We _____ to find the way home. **tried   tryed**

d I _____ to the question the teacher asked. **replied   replyed**

e The prince _____ the princess. **marryed   married**

f Kate was bursting with _____ when she saw her present. **happiness   happyness**

g Dad carried the _____ bag. **heavyest   heaviest**

h My kitten is _____ than all the others. **prettier   prettyer**

i He was _____ of the spider. **terrifyed   terrified**

14

Connectives in complex sentences

A complex sentence has more than one clause. Connective words and phrases can be used to join these two clauses together.

It was my birthday, **so** I had a party.

first clause   second clause

 I Underline the connective word or phrase in each of these complex sentences.

a I did my homework while Dad cooked tea.

b Sally wore her coat, because it was cold.

c We were late, so we had to run.

d Marc got into trouble, because of his untidy bedroom.

e I love tennis, but netball is better.

f I enjoyed the film, although I had seen it before.

g We had our breakfast before we went to school.

h Eva saved her pocket money, so she could buy the CD.

II Write each pair of simple sentences again as one complex sentence, joined by a connective from the box.

although	so	while	before	but	because

a I had a lie in. It was Saturday.

_____

b It was hot. We bought some ice creams.

_____

c Max counted to twenty. His friends hid.

_____

d We packed our suitcase. We left for the airport.

_____

e Susie won second prize. Alice won first prize.

_____

f John drank his tea quickly. It was hot.

_____

Contracting sentences

Sometimes, we can take the really important information from a piece of writing, then write it again in a form we can use more quickly.

If we make **notes**, we just write down key words that will jog our memory later. Notes don't have to be complete sentences.

If we write a **summary**, we rewrite the most important information in complete sentences.

I **Underline the key words in this piece of writing.**

The Vikings invaded Britain more than a thousand years ago. They sailed from Sweden, Norway and Denmark in longboats, and raided the coasts and rivers of the United Kingdom. Many also settled here and farmed the land. Viking families lived in houses made from wood, stone or turf, with a hole in the roof to let out the smoke from the cooking fires. They believed in many gods, but the most popular were Odin, the wise and one-eyed, and Thor, the god of thunder.

II **Now write a set of notes, and a summary, of the piece of writing using the words you have just underlined to help you.**

Notes:

_____

_____

_____

_____

_____

_____

_____

Summary:

_____

_____

_____

_____

_____

_____

Conditionals

We use conditionals to show that one thing happening depends on something else.

We'll go **if** there's time.

 Underline the conditionals in these sentences.

a If you use matches, you might burn yourself.

b Going to the fair would be brilliant.

c I can come to your party, if I finish my homework.

d If we're not greedy, we'll have enough sweets for all of us.

e Missing the bus might make us late for school.

f I'll feel better after I've had something to eat.

g When my bike is mended, I'm going for a ride.

h When I'm older, I can stay up late.

i When I go to bed, I'll read my book.

Use the conditionals in bold to help you write sensible endings for these sentences.

a **If** it is raining _____.

b **Unless** you're too tired _____.

c **Should** I win the competition _____.

d **When** it is cold _____.

e Cheating in the test **might** _____.

f Helping Mum **should** _____.

g Going to bed early **might** _____.

h Having six kittens **would be** _____.

i I will get my allowance **if** I _____.

j **When** we get home _____.

Constructing arguments

When you are writing an argument, you will want to persuade your readers to agree with your point of view.

If you think about the objections your readers might have to your idea, you can include answers to them in your argument.

> **Although most children don't like doing homework,** it does help them to practise what they have learnt at school.

You can also provide evidence to support your view.

> **A survey at our school found** that children who do their homework are more likely to do well in their tests.

Imagine you are going to write an argument in favour of wearing school uniform. Look at the pieces of fictional evidence below. Underline the ones that could help to support your argument.

a The cost of school uniform has risen by 40%.

b Reports show that schools with uniforms have less bullying because all the children are wearing the same.

c School clothing is specially designed to be durable and easy to care for.

d Research by clothing stores argues that fashion clothing lets children express their personalities.

e About 60% of children say they have less fashion clothing because their parents have to buy uniform as well.

f A survey of headteachers says that schools with uniforms have a higher profile in the local community.

g Motoring groups warn that the dark colour of most winter school uniforms makes it hard for children to be seen by motorists at night.

Write down three objections your readers may have against wearing uniform and how you could answer them in your argument.

Your readers may argue	You could answer
a	
b	
c	

Inventing words

Most of the words we use can be found in the dictionary, but occasionally we can make up our own words, using prefixes and suffixes with set meanings.

micro + phobia = microphobia

small   fear   fear of small things

I   Imagine you are writing a science fiction story based in the future. Lots of the things you need to write about haven't been invented yet, so there are no words for them. Look at the meanings of the suffixes and prefixes in the box. Then use them to help you invent words for these things.

scope = look	phobia = fear	hydro = water	port = carry	phile = love
micro = small	graph = write	bi = two	octo = eight	tele = far off
audi = hear	phone = sound	photo = light	auto = self	

a   A device that allows you to look in eight different directions at once.   _____

b   A station for underwater travel.   _____

c   An instrument that allows you to write very small, to save space.   _____

d   A camera that takes two pictures of you at the same time.   _____

e   A fear of things far away.   _____

f   A machine that creates a written record of sounds.   _____

g   A way of transporting objects and people in a beam of light.   _____

h   A machine which allows the same sound to be played in two different places at the same time.   _____

II   Use the words in the box above to help you work out what these made up words might mean.

a   octophone _____

b   photophile _____

c   microport _____

d   audiophobe _____

e   hydrophile _____

f   autoscope _____

Word games

Playing words games can improve your spelling and help you to learn new words.

I Find these sporting words in the word search grid. When you have finished, rearrange the red letters to make the name of a popular team game.

a hockey

b netball

c squash

d swimming

e athletics

f football

g tennis

h cricket

i badminton

j rounders

s	p	e	t	e	n	n	i	s	h	n
n	a	h	m	u	z	m	j	n	v	o
t	r	o	u	n	d	e	r	s	k	t
s	b	c	s	w	e	v	e	q	a	n
w	c	k	l	y	f	b	l	u	w	i
i	n	e	t	b	a	l	l	a	n	m
m	d	y	f	k	t	r	i	s	x	d
m	y	s	c	i	t	e	l	h	t	a
i	p	x	s	r	x	a	h	i	g	b
n	g	u	c	r	i	c	k	e	t	j
g	f	o	o	t	b	a	l	l	d	b
w	c	n	t	z	o	v	c	q	d	q

The mystery sport is ____ ____ ____ ____ ____.

II Use the clues to help you unscramble each group of letters into two words.

a tacbhalire — You'll find these in the dining room. — _table_ _chair_

b kfnioferk — You eat with these. — _____ _____

c appepalre — Both fruits that grow on trees. — _____ _____

d mosotanrs — You'll see these in the night sky. — _____ _____

e shboeoosts — You wear these on your feet. — _____ _____

f bmaogoazkine — You might read these. — _____ _____

g cchhaeleske — These things are very different! — _____ _____

h sapltepper — You put these on your food. — _____ _____

20

Formal writing

The language we use when we speak to each other is informal.

> Do you want to come to my party?

Official written language is much more formal.

> Jay requests the pleasure of your company at her party.

 Draw lines to match up the formal language with the less formal version on the signs.

a Breakages must be purchased.

b Kindly refrain from walking on the grass.

c Children are not permitted on the premises.

d Parking is prohibited.

e Kindly complete your purchases as the store is closing.

f Please submit all outstanding monies due immediately.

g Trespassing is forbidden.

> Please don't walk on the grass
>
> NO PARKING
>
> PLEASE PAY FOR YOUR SHOPPING AS THE STORE IS CLOSING
>
> You mustn't be here without permission
>
> PLEASE HAND OVER ALL THE MONEY YOU OWE RIGHT NOW!
>
> CHILDREN ARE NOT ALLOWED IN HERE
>
> YOU MUST PAY FOR ANYTHING YOU BREAK.

Use informal language to write down what these sentences mean.

a Patrons are politely requested to vacate the premises promptly at 6 o'clock.

_____

b Non-compliance with club rules will invalidate membership.

_____

c Drivers failing to adhere to stated speed restrictions will be liable to a fine.

_____

d Travellers must be able to present a valid ticket upon request.

_____

e The management accepts no responsibility for property lost or damaged.

_____

f Refunds will only be made for faulty or damaged goods.

_____

Play scripts

Plays tell a story just like a piece of narrative writing, but most plays don't have a narrator to move the story along.

What the characters say and do on stage tells the story. The script contains the characters' lines and stage directions to tell them what to do.

I Imagine you are writing a film or TV script based on the section of story below. Write a description of the footpath, plus stage directions for Andy and Calum.

Andy and Calum hurried along the footpath. The moon that had been shining so brightly before had disappeared behind a cloud. 'Hurry!' said Andy. 'Let's get out of here.'

'What was that?' hissed Calum, spinning round to look behind them.

Setting: _____

_____

_____

_____

Stage directions for Andy: _____

_____

Stage directions for Calum: _____

_____

II Write a section of play script based on the passage from the story. Include the next few lines, where we discover what or who is following the boys down the path.

_____

_____

_____

_____

_____

_____

_____

_____

Prepositions

Prepositions are words like **at**, **in** or **to**. They can describe position, direction or time.

We went out **at** lunchtime.

He sat **on** the sofa.

 Circle the preposition in these sentence.

a It rained during the night.

b The cat ran up the tree.

c We went to the cinema.

d I waited behind you in the queue.

e Chloe sat on the stool.

f Jack climbed over the fence.

g The missing pen was under my bed.

h We are visiting friends on Friday.

 Imagine you are watching a fallen leaf blowing in the wind. Write a short paragraph about its journey to the ground, using each of the prepositions in the box.

| down | through | up | under | across | between | onto | around |

_____

_____

_____

_____

_____

_____

_____

_____

_____

_____

_____

Mnemonics

Mnemonics are slogans or phrases we can use to help us remember how to spell tricky words.

Some focus on a particular part of a word we find difficult.

separate

move **a**way

We can also make them up to help us remember whole words.

knight

king's **n**aughty **i**mps **g**o **h**ome **t**onight

I Choose the word from the box that you think each of these mnemonics could help you to remember.

| beauty | Wednesday | receipt | bought | fluoride | sweet | typical | receive |

a Tiny yellow people ice cakes a lot. _____

b Fat lazy uncles' ogres race inside demanding eggs. _____

c Witches eat dead nettles every single day. _____

d Blue otters under green hats trade. _____

e Bonny elves await ugly trolls yodelling. _____

f Ruby earrings can even interest vain elephants. _____

g Sugary wonderful exciting edible treat. _____

h Rats eat chocolate eggs in private tunnels. _____

II Write mnemonics for these words.

a conscious _____

b ambitious _____

c jealous _____

d politician _____

e frightened _____

f astronaut _____

g fiery _____

h placate _____

Using dictionaries

Dictionaries can help us to find out more about the spelling and meaning of groups of words with the same prefix.

I

Write down three words that begin with each of the prefixes below. Use a dictionary to look up the meanings, then use the definitions to help you work out what each prefix means.

a mis = _____

_____

_____

_____

b ex = _____

_____

_____

_____

c sub = _____

_____

_____

_____

II

The words that match the three definitions in each group below share the same prefix. Write down the three words. Use a dictionary to check the meanings.

a to stop something from happening _____

to say what will happen in the future _____

to get something ready _____

b to make again _____

to put something back _____

to mend _____

c not to agree _____

to get rid of _____

to vanish _____

Direct and reported speech

When we are writing, we often need to record what people say.

Direct speech quotes the actual words the person says. We put it between speech marks.

'Look at my new skates,' said Leo.

Reported speech reports what someone says, but doesn't use their exact words.

She said she would be late.

I Turn the speech bubbles into sentences with direct speech.

Shall we go to the zoo Ryan?

I'd love to Chloe. When shall we go?

Let's go on Thursday. We could go with Sam.

Good idea! I'll ask him if he can come.

_____

_____

_____

_____

II Rewrite these pieces of direct speech, as reported speech.

a Kate said, 'Fancy going bowling?'

_____

b 'Where's my school bag?' asked Jake.

_____

c 'Please be back by 6 o'clock,' said Mum.

_____

d Jamie said, 'I'm going to the beach tomorrow!'

_____

e Sally asked, 'Will we get there in time?'

_____

f 'Happy birthday!' shouted the twins.

_____

More spelling rules

We can use spelling rules to help us spell words where i and e appear together.

Many words have ie.

> tie   quiet

c is usually followed by ei: i before e, except after c

> conceit   receive

Other words with ei tend to have a long 'a' sound.

> vein   weigh

 Choose the correctly spelt words from each set in bold to complete these sentences.

a I ate two _____ of cake. **peices   pieces**

b I kept the _____, so I could take the dress back if it didn't fit. **receipt   reciept**

c A spider has _____ legs. **ieght   eight**

d Indira is my best _____. **friend   freind**

e My Dad loves apple _____. **pie   pei**

f Water was pouring through the _____. **ceiling   cieling**

g The bride wore a long white _____. **viel   veil**

h The _____ stole my bike. **thief   theif**

i We borrowed some eggs from our _____. **nieghbour   neighbour**

j On holiday, we visited a _____ castle. **medieval   medeival**

Underline the misspelt words in this piece of writing. Watch out for exceptions to the rules!

I love going to the museum. They have an anceint sheild that belonged to a brave knight during the riegn of a famous medeival king. They also have his sword, which is sharp enough to peirce armour. There's a modern copy too, so you can feel the wieght of it.

Also in the museum is a model of an Iron Age tribal cheif, and information about the beleifs his people held. You can watch a reconstruction of one of their battles, with feirce warriors racing across a feild shreiking. It really changed my veiw of history.

Similes

Similes create a picture in your reader's mind by comparing one thing to another, using the word **as** or **like**.

as weak **as** a lamb

sleeping **like** a baby

I Pick a noun from the box to complete these well-known similes.

| chimney | bee | log | wind | fish | lark | hills | ox | bat | mouse |

a as old as the _____

b as quiet as a _____

c as strong as an _____

d as blind as a _____

e as busy as a _____

f smoking like a _____

g run like the _____

h sing like a _____

i swims like a _____

j sleeping like a _____

II Think of ways to complete these similes.

a as _____ as a bear

b as bright as a _____

c as _____ as ice

d as young as _____

e eating like a _____

f jumping like _____

g _____ like thunder

h _____ like a horse

Rhyme and assonance

Rhyme and assonance can both be very effective in poetry and stories.

Assonance is where two or more words contain the same vowel sound. The words may also rhyme, but they don't have to.

> sly   crime   resign

Rhyming words end with the same sound. Groups of rhyming words are also examples of assonance, because they contain the same vowel sound.

> tongue   hung   young

I The groups of words below are all examples of assonance. Underline the groups that don't rhyme.

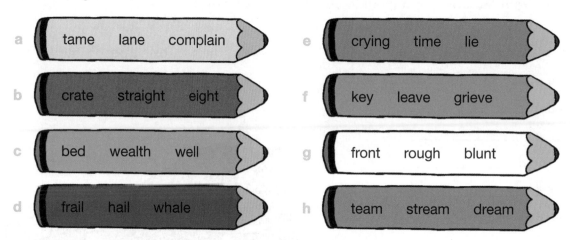

a tame   lane   complain

b crate   straight   eight

c bed   wealth   well

d frail   hail   whale

e crying   time   lie

f key   leave   grieve

g front   rough   blunt

h team   stream   dream

II For each of the words below, write down one example of rhyme and one of assonance. The first has been done for you.

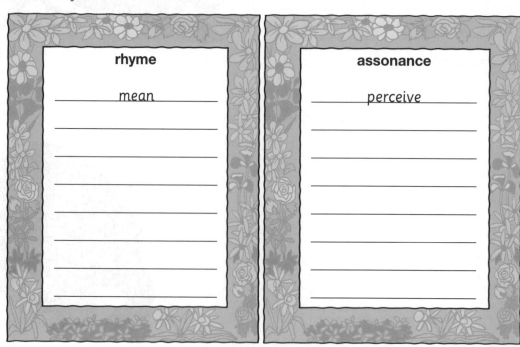

	rhyme	assonance
a clean	mean	perceive
b out		
c home		
d child		
e train		
f buy		
g bread		
h bold		

Narrator

When we read a story, it is the **narrator's** viewpoint we are reading.

Sometimes the narrator is one of the characters in the story.

> He tore my magazine, so I'm taking his precious car. It's as simple as that.

Sometimes the narrator is not in the story at all.

> Cassie was furious with Joe, and paid him back by taking his favourite toy car.

Who the narrator is determines how we see the story.

I In the short section of story below, the narrator is not part of the story. Look at what Cassie and Joe say, and the words they use. Then answer the questions about what you think they might be like.

Joe marched into Cassie's room and grabbed his toy car. 'It's mine!' he shouted, and kicked over the neat pile of books Cassie had just made. 'Get out, brat,' squealed Cassie, throwing her shoe at him.
'I'm telling Mummy,' he yelled back.

But he didn't tell Mum. He just sat on his bed, blinking back tears, and wishing he was old enough to really teach Cassie a lesson.

a How old do you think Joe is? _____

b Is he older, or younger, than Cassie? _____

c How old might Cassie be? _____

d What might the relationship be between Cassie and Joe? _____

e Do you think they often argue like this? _____

II Write the story again twice, first with Joe as the narrator, then Cassie. Try to write it using the kinds of words each character might use if they were telling the story directly to you.

Joe's story:

_____

_____

_____

_____

Cassie's story:

_____

_____

_____

Another spelling rule

Using a spelling rule can help us add suffixes to words ending in a modifying e.

A modifying e changes the vowel sound in the middle of a word, making it a long, drawn-out sound.

h**o**p	h**o**pe
short **o** sound	long **oe** sound

If the suffix you want to add starts with a vowel, you must remove the modifying e from the base word first.

make + ing = making

If the suffix starts with a consonant, you keep the e and just add the suffix.

love + ly = lovely

 I Add the suffixes in the table to each of these words.

	+ ing	+ ed	+ ful	+ less
a shame	_____	_____	_____	_____
b hope	_____	_____	_____	_____
c care	_____	_____	_____	_____
d use	_____	_____	_____	_____

II Underline the misspelt word in each sentence. Then write the correct spelling.

a My aunt is liveing in Australia. _____

b I have savd enough money for a new bike. _____

c Craig is makeing a model aeroplane. _____

d Dad has takn my brother to watch the football. _____

e Our new puppy is so adoreable. _____

f We chose the niceest Christmas tree. _____

g It's safest to walk on the pavment. _____

h Dawn's singing is more tunful than mine. _____

i I love bakeing cakes. _____

j My baby sister is very livly. _____

ANSWERS

Page 2

I er: interest, desperate, generally, generous, offering, literature
en: deafening, widening

II ary: stationary, boundary, voluntary
ory: factory, category, history
ery: jewellery, stationery, lottery
erence: reference, conference, difference

Page 3

I audi: audible, audience, audition
trans: transport, transplant, transfer
re: reply, reconsider, repeat
prim: prime, primate, primary
pre: preview, prevent, prehistoric

II
a periscope
b seclude
c transport
d teleport or telescope
e include
f microscope
g import
h conclude

Page 4

I
a whenever
b meanwhile
c moreover
d whereas or wherever
e furthermore
f nonetheless
g notwithstanding
h henceforward

II
a as well as
b despite
c as a result
d at the same time
e from now on
f every time
g in order that
h another thing

Page 5

I
a stay
b listen to
c look at
d truly
e there
f from where
g here
h you

II
a near
b enemy
c beautiful
d says
e you or the
f towards what place
g please
h go away!

Page 6

I
a run
b try
c sing
d swim
e flies
f washes
g sleeps
h plays

II
a teacher
b cats
c boy
d horses
e brother
f girls
g trains
h shop

Page 7

I The active verbs are: a, b, e, g, h
The passive verbs are: c, d, f, i, j

II
a The cat chased the mouse.
b The rain soaked my clothes.
c Sam found the missing book.
d Jo opened the door.
e The paperboy delivered my magazine.
f The teacher marked our test papers.

Page 8

I
a <u>Who is that</u>, knocking at the door?
b <u>I felt ill</u>, so I went to bed.
c <u>We went swimming</u> in the river.
d <u>It was dark</u> when we got home.
e <u>We went to Italy</u> for our holiday.
f <u>I broke the vase</u> when I was dusting.
g <u>Mum made me a cake</u> for my birthday.
h <u>The car broke down</u>, because it had run out of petrol.
i <u>Gran went shopping</u> to buy some slippers.
j <u>I drew a picture</u> to hang on the wall.

II Many answers are possible.

Page 9

I
a The cat (a tabby) curled up and went to sleep.
b The packed lunch (a ham sandwich) was delicious.
c After school (but before tea) we played in the park.
d The cold rain (and freezing wind) kept us indoors.
e My little brother's hair (which he cut himself) looks dreadful.
f The football (kicked by Paul) flew over the fence.

II
a My best friend (who is ten) is called Lily.
b The old dog was dirty (and smelly).
c Pink (but not pale pink) is my favourite colour. Or,
Pink is my favourite colour (but not pale pink).
d My new coat (bought yesterday) is really warm.
e My new school (where I'm going in September) is really big.
f The school holiday (which starts next week) is going to be great.

Page 10

I We sat by the ruined cottage to have our picnic. The sun <u>smiled down</u> on us, and birds <u>chattered</u> in the trees. All around us, buttercups <u>danced</u> in the breeze, and the <u>nodding</u> branches of a willow tree sheltered us from the <u>fierce</u> sun. The broken windows of the deserted cottage <u>stared silently</u> towards the <u>sleeping</u> hills in the distance, and the wind <u>whispered</u> secrets through the empty rooms.

II Many answers are possible.

Page 11

I Examples of biography are: a, d, f.
Examples of autobiography are: b, c, e.

II Exact answers may vary.
When she was eight, she was sent to a strict girls' boarding school. She missed her family terribly and never settled into school life, so she was thrilled when the war came and she was evacuated to Wales with her three brothers. For the next four years they lived on a farm, so it was a dreadful shock for her to return to post-war London, and to school.

Page 12

I
a The grass is always greener on the other side.
b The early bird catches the worm.
c A bird in the hand is worth two in the bush.
d Great minds think alike.
e Every cloud has a silver lining.
f A bad workman blames his tools.
g Many a true word is said in jest.
h Let sleeping dogs lie.

II Exact wording may vary.
a A job is easier if shared between many people.
b Don't risk everything on one go.
c A problem is easier to solve if two people work together.
d Mending things sooner saves time in the long run.
e From one unpleasant situation to another.
f Never assume things will be as you expect.
g Think ahead before you take a big decision.

Page 13

I The adverbs are:
a silently
b outside
c quickly
d never
e later
f there
g slowly
h angrily
i unsteadily
j always

II
a quickly
b here
c brightly
d always
e nearly
f happily
g soundly
h soon

Page 14

I
a emptiness
b frying
c denied
d readily
e sleepily
f windier
g silliness
h carrying
i friendly

II
a lazily
b hungrily
c tried
d replied
e married
f happiness
g heaviest
h prettier
i terrified

Page 15

I
a while
b because
c so
d because of
e but
f although
g before
h so

II
a because
b so
c while
d before
e but
f although or while

Page 16

I Answers may vary slightly.
The <u>Vikings invaded Britain</u> more than a thousand years ago. They sailed from <u>Sweden, Norway and Denmark</u> in <u>longboats</u>, and raided the <u>coasts and rivers</u> of the United Kingdom. Many also settled here and <u>farmed</u> the land. Viking families lived in <u>houses</u> made from <u>wood,</u>

stone or turf, with a hole in the roof to let out the smoke from the cooking fires. They believed in many gods, but the most popular were Odin, the wise and one-eyed, and Thor, the god of thunder.

II Many answers are possible.

Page 17

I a If you use matches, you might burn yourself.
  b Going to the fair would be brilliant.
  c I can come to your party, if I finish my homework.
  d If we're not greedy, we'll have enough sweets for all of us.
  e Missing the bus might make us late for school.
  f I'll feel better after I've had something to eat.
  g When my bike is mended, I'm going for a ride.
  h When I'm older, I can stay up late.
  i When I go to bed, I'll read my book.

II Many answers are possible.

Page 18

I Evidence in favour of school uniforms is: b, c, f.

II Many answers are possible.

Page 19

I Most likely answers are:
  a octoscope
  b hydroport
  c micrograph
  d biphoto
  e telephobia
  f phonograph
  g photoport
  h biphone

II Answers may vary.
  a A machine which creates eight sounds.
  b A person who loves light.
  c A machine that transports small things.
  d A person who hates sound.
  e A person who loves water.
  f A mirror.

Page 20

I

s	p	e	t	e	n	n	i	s	h	n
n	a	h	m	u	z	m	j	n	v	o
t	r	o	u	n	d	e	r	s	k	t
s	b	c	s	w	e	v	e	q	a	n
w	c	k	l	y	f	b	l	u	w	i
i	n	e	t	b	a	l	l	a	n	m
m	d	y	f	k	t	r	i	s	x	d
m	y	s	c	i	t	e	l	h	t	a
i	p	x	s	r	x	a	h	i	g	b
n	g	u	c	r	i	c	k	e	t	j
g	f	o	o	t	b	a	l	l	d	b
w	c	p	t	z	o	y	c	q	d	q

The mystery word is rugby.

II a table chair   e shoes boots
  b knife fork   f book magazine
  c apple pear   g chalk cheese
  d moon stars   h salt pepper

Page 21

I a You must pay for anything you break.
  b Please don't walk on the grass.
  c Children are not allowed in here.
  d No parking.
  e Please pay for your shopping as the store is closing.
  f Please hand over all the money you owe right now!
  g You mustn't be here without permission.

II Exact answers may vary.
  a Customers are asked to leave by 6 o'clock.
  b If you break the rules you can't be a member of the club any more.
  c Drivers who go too fast will have to pay a fine.
  d Travellers must be able to show they have a ticket.
  e The management won't take the blame if your things are lost or broken.
  f You can only get your money back if what you have bought doesn't work or is damaged.

Page 22

I Many answers are possible.

II Many answers are possible.

Page 23

I The prepositions are:
  a during   d behind, in   g under
  b up   e on   h on
  c to   f over

II Many answers are possible.

Page 24

I a typical   e beauty
  b fluoride   f receive
  c Wednesday   g sweet
  d bought   h receipt

II Many answers are possible.

Page 25

I a mis = wrong or bad
  b ex = outside of, from
  c sub = under

II a prevent, predict, prepare
  b remake or rebuild, replace, repair
  c disagree, dispose or discard, disappear

Page 26

I Exact wording may vary.
  'Shall we go to the zoo?' asked Chloe.
  'I'd love to. When shall we go?' said Ryan.
  'Let's go on Thursday. We could go with Sam,' replied Chloe.
  'Good idea! I'll ask him if he can come,' said Ryan.

II Exact wording may vary.
  a Kate asked if I'd like to go bowling.
  b Jake asked where his school bag was.
  c Mum said we must be back by 6 o'clock.
  d Jamie said he was going to the beach tomorrow.
  e Sally asked if we would get there in time.
  f The twins shouted happy birthday.

Page 27

I The correctly spelt words are:
  a pieces   f ceiling
  b receipt   g veil
  c eight   h thief
  d friend   i neighbour
  e pie   j medieval

II I love going to the museum. They have an anceint sheild that belonged to a brave knight during the riegn of a famous medeival king. They also have his sword, which is sharp enough to peirce armour. There's a modern copy too, so you can feel the wieght of it.
Also in the museum is a model of an Iron Age tribal cheif, and information about the beleifs his people held. You can watch a reconstruction of one of their battles, with feirce warriors racing across a feild shreiking. It really changed my veiw of history.

Page 28

I a hills   f chimney
  b mouse   g wind
  c ox   h lark
  d bat   i fish
  e bee   j log

II Many answers are possible.

Page 29

I The groups that don't rhyme are: a, c, e, f, g.

II Many answers are possible.

Page 30

I a Perhaps around five or six.
  b Younger.
  c Perhaps around 10 or 11.
  d Brother and sister.
  e Yes.

II Many answers are possible.

Page 31

I a shaming shamed shameful shameless
  b hoping hoped hopeful hopeless
  c caring cared careful careless
  d using used useful useless

II The misspelt words are:
  a liveing   f niceest
  b savd   g pavment
  c makeing   h tunful
  d takn   i bakeing
  e adoreable   j livly
  The correct spellings are:
  a living   f nicest
  b saved   g pavement
  c making   h tuneful
  d taken   i baking
  e adorable   j lively

Test 1 Unstressed vowels

Some **vowels** in longer words are **not stressed** and are difficult to hear.

envelope

Fill in the missing vowels.

1. di____mond

2. accident____l

3. entr____nce

4. diff____rent

5. deod____rant

6. myst____ry

7. cru____l

8. int____resting

9. eff____rt

10. monast____ry

11. lunch____on

12. sep____rate

13. butt____n

14. skel____ton

15. ph____tographer

Colour in your score

Test 1

Test 2 Root words

A **root word** is a word to which **prefixes** or **suffixes** may be added. Sometimes the root word is **easy** to see. Sometimes the root word is **harder** to work out.

bicycle (root word = cycle)   beautiful (root word = beauty)

Work out the root word for each of these words.

1. befriend _____

2. assistance _____

3. centimetre _____

4. disability _____

5. beggar _____

6. engineer _____

7. exchange _____

8. kingdom _____

9. brightness _____

10. imperfect _____

11. prefix _____

12. service _____

13. superman _____

14. duckling _____

15. withhold _____

Colour in your score

Test 2

A **dash** holds words apart. It is stronger than a comma but is not as strong as a full stop.

I have got a new bike – a mountain bike.

Decide where to put the dash in each sentence.

1. I had my favourite meal spaghetti.

2. I love apples Ben hates them!

3. One boy looked strange he was wearing a mask.

4. I won a prize for coming first in spelling.

5. My uncle appeared laughing as usual.

6. Christopher Wren built a famous cathedral St Paul's.

7. Mr Smith has a sports car a silver one.

8. I love music especially pop music.

9. On the sand I found something interesting an old chest.

10. Work hard or you will never get a good job!

11. I know someone very brave my friend Sarah.

12. Tom collects insects especially beetles.

13. Mount Pico is in the Azores a group of islands.

14. I saw a good programme last night a monster film.

15. My room overlooks a wood a small dark wood.

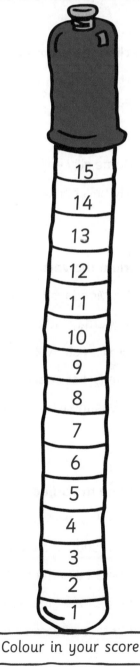

15
14
13
12
11
10
9
8
7
6
5
4
3
2
1

Colour in your score

Test 4 Parts of speech

Words may be divided into groups called **parts of speech**. Three important parts of speech are **nouns**, **verbs** and **adjectives**.

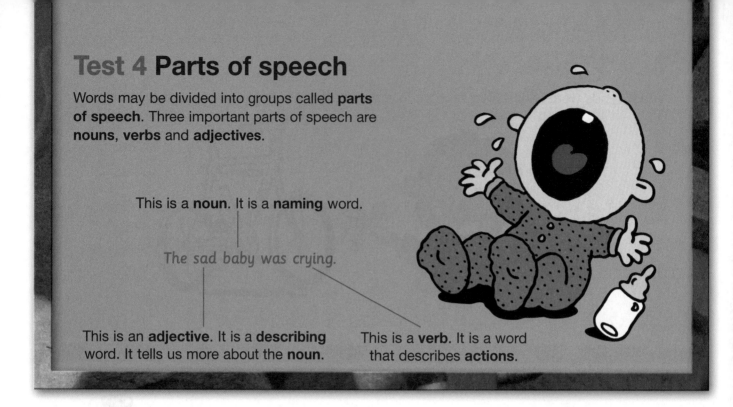

This is a **noun**. It is a **naming** word.

The sad baby was crying.

This is an **adjective**. It is a **describing** word. It tells us more about the **noun**.

This is a **verb**. It is a word that describes **actions**.

Underline the noun in each sentence.

1. The red door was shut.

2. The poor old man had to sit down.

3. The wind howled and howled.

4. Some silly children were giggling.

5. My new car was metallic silver.

Underline the verb in each sentence.

6. On Mondays I always ride my bike.

7. Yesterday I ate fifteen biscuits!

8. Next week I will try much harder.

9. Mrs Baker cooked a lovely casserole.

10. Cross the road carefully.

Underline the adjective in each sentence.

11. The floor was slippery.

12. The rough sea crashed against the cliffs.

13. Some colourful birds landed in the garden.

14. In the forest it is scary.

15. My favourite uncle came to see me.

Colour in your score

Test 4

Test 5 Connectives

We sometimes join two **clause**s together by using a **connective**.

I like the summer   because   I go on holiday then.

clause 1   connective   clause 2

Choose the best connective to join each pair of clauses.

1. He was not tired _____ he had to go to bed. (nevertheless/and)

2. I couldn't decide whether to go _____ stay. (and/or)

3. She put up her umbrella _____ it was raining. (so that/because)

4. We stopped for a cup of tea _____ we were early. (as/so)

5. I ate my lunch _____ I went out. (because/before)

6. The cat chased the birds _____ they landed. (since/when)

7. I turned up the radio _____ I could hear it. (as/so that)

8. I won't go out _____ it is raining. (and/if)

9. If you are late _____ you will get into trouble. (when/then)

10. I had a wash _____ I went to the party. (in case/until)

11. I shouted _____ someone heard me. (until/because)

12. I could not do it _____ hard I tried. (however/in case)

13. I don't like cheese _____ my mum does. (and/but)

14. We went home _____ the match finished. (as soon as/until)

15. We ran fast _____ we were late. (after/because)

Colour in your score

Test 5

Test 6 Prefixes and suffixes

We add **prefixes** and **suffixes** to words to **change their meanings**.

accurate – **in**accurate

A **prefix** is added to the **beginning** of a word. It does **not** change the spelling of the root word.

happy – happi**ness**

A **suffix** is added to the **end** of a word. It may **sometimes** change the spelling of the root word.

Choose the correct prefix to complete each word.

1. _____graph (ex/auto)

2. _____legal (im/il)

3. _____port (de/mal)

4. _____patient (in/im)

5. _____approve (for/dis)

6. _____behave (dis/mis)

7. _____bark (em/en)

8. _____arrange (pre/pro)

Add the suffix to each root word. Write the word you make.

9. confide (ence) _____

10. bake (ery) _____

11. communicate (ion) _____

12. study (ent) _____

13. replace (ment) _____

14. serve (ice) _____

15. friendly (ness) _____

15
14
13
12
11
10
9
8
7
6
5
4
3
2
1

Colour in your score

Test 6

Test 7 Active and passive verbs

The footballer kicked the ball.
A verb is **active** when the subject of the sentence does the action.

The ball was kicked by the footballer.
A verb is **passive** when the subject of the sentence has the action done to it.

Decide if the verb in each sentence is active or passive.

1. The child wrote a story. _____

2. The books were written by the author. _____

3. The man rode his mountain bike. _____

4. The telephone was answered by the lady. _____

5. The shoes were worn by Sarah. _____

6. The squirrel climbed the tree. _____

7. The lion chased the antelope. _____

8. The cakes were eaten by Mrs Sallis. _____

9. I received a present yesterday. _____

10. The sword was waved by the pirate. _____

11. The farmer collected the eggs. _____

12. The snake slid along the ground. _____

13. The nest was made by the bird. _____

14. The song was sung by the pop singer. _____

15. I telephoned my friend. _____

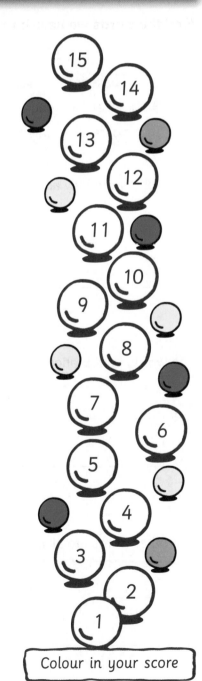

Colour in your score

Test 7

Test 8 Where do our words come from?

English is not just **one language**. It is made up of words taken from many **other languages**.

pizza (Italian)

yacht (Dutch)

vase (French)

Find the words we have borrowed from other languages.

ballerina   skipper   buffet   piano   cabaret

bracket   spaghetti   sketch   schooner   bouquet

opera   confetti   smuggle   landscape   duvet

The words from Italy all end in a vowel other than **e**.

1. _____   2. _____   3. _____

4. _____   5. _____

The words from France all end in **et**.

6. _____   7. _____   8. _____

9. _____   10. _____

The other words are all Dutch words.

11. _____   12. _____   13. _____

14. _____   15. _____

Colour in your score

15 14 13 12 11 10 9 8 7 6 5 4 3 2 1

Test 8

Test 9 Mnemonics

A **mnemonic** is a way of remembering the spelling of tricky words.

*I have **a chest** ache*

ambitious   believe   business   breadth

cereal   chocolate   conscience   government

island   knowledge   mathematics

piece   separate   soldier   whole

Find the word with the following word 'hiding' in it.

1. know _____   9. rat _____

2. lie _____   10. bread _____

3. them _____   11. science _____

4. pie _____   12. who _____

5. bit _____   13. is _____

6. late _____   14. real _____

7. bus _____   15. die _____

8. men _____

Colour in your score

Test 9

Test 10 Punctuation

Punctuation marks help us **make sense** of what we read. Where we put punctuation marks can make a difference!

I wore a hat. On my head
I wore some boots.

I wore a hat on my head.
I wore some boots.

Fill in the missing punctuation marks.

1. Dr Turner___s car was green.

2. Mrs Brown, who was getting angry___ shouted loudly.

3. "Don___t cross the busy road," Mrs Smith warned Tom.

4. Do you like oranges or lemons best___

5. During the night___ it rained heavily.

6. "Where's my dinner?___ the giant roared.

7. "I hate sprouts___" Sam shouted.

8. My brother hates music___ but I love it.

9. In my pocket I had a coin, a sweet___ a tissue and a badge.

10. The teachers___ room is next to the office.

11. Where are you going___

12. I___m nearly eleven.

13. The film doesn___t begin for an hour.

14. "Hands up___" the robber shouted.

15. ___My job can be dangerous," the police officer said.

Colour in your score

Test 10

Test 11 Word origins

The English language has been influenced by **many other languages**. Understanding the **origins** of words sometimes helps us to spell them.

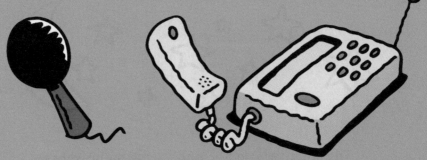

The word **phone** comes from a Greek word meaning **sound**.

micro**phone**   tele**phone**

---

spectator   liberty   signal   liberal   spectacles
audience   liberate   audible   script   signature
describe   scribble   spectacular   auditorium   design

Write some English words we get from these Latin words.

signum (meaning a sign)

1. _____   2. _____   3. _____

liber (meaning free)

4. _____   5. _____   6. _____

audio (meaning I hear)

7. _____   8. _____   9. _____

scribo (meaning I write)

10. _____   11. _____   12. _____

specto (meaning I watch)

13. _____   14. _____   15. _____

15 14 13 12 11 10 9 8 7 6 5 4 3 2 1

Colour in your score

Test 12 Complex sentences

A **clause** is a **group of words** which can be used as a **whole sentence** or as **part of a sentence**. Many sentences contain **more than one** clause.

This sentence contains two clauses.

The stars twinkled   *and*   *the moon shone.*

clause 1   clause 2

Write and say how many clauses there are in each sentence. (1 or 2)

1. I like West Highland Terrier dogs. _____

2. Some cats stay out all night. _____

3. I fell over while we were playing. _____

4. The cat chased the birds that landed on the grass. _____

5. I posted the letter in the post box. _____

6. I bought the comic from the shop. _____

7. When the wind blew the trees swayed. _____

8. Last night I had stomach ache after I ate my tea. _____

9. Cows moo but don't bark. _____

10. Nelson's Column stands in the middle of London. _____

11. The man got stuck when the lift doors closed. _____

12. I went to Spain and visited Madrid. _____

13. My budgie escaped when I left its cage open. _____

14. The lady paid for her hat and left the shop. _____

15. The ugly troll waited patiently under the bridge. _____

Colour in your score

Test 12

Test 13 Proverbs

A **proverb** is a **wise saying** that has been around for a **long time**.

Don't count your chickens before they're hatched.

Match up the beginning and ending of each proverb.

1. Absence makes the heart   than words.

2. Beggars can't be   twice shy.

3. Actions speak louder   never.

4. Birds of a feather   less speed.

5. Once bitten,   choosers.

6. Every cloud has   out of mind.

7. Too many cooks   you leap.

8. Don't put all your eggs   grow fonder.

9. More haste,   than one.

10. Make hay while   flock together.

11. Two heads are better   a silver lining.

12. Better late than   in one basket.

13. Look before   the sun shines.

14. Out of sight,   saves nine.

15. A stitch in time   spoil the broth.

Colour in your score

Test 14 Syllables

Words can be broken down into smaller parts, called **syllables**.

um / brel / la   (3 syllables)

Think of a suitable second syllable for each word. Write the words you make.

1. de + _____ + mine =   _____

2. u + _____ + form =   _____

3. hos + _____ + al =   _____

4. ex + _____ + lent =   _____

5. at + _____ + tion =   _____

6. dif + _____ + ent =   _____

7. ad + _____ + ture =   _____

8. syl + _____ + le =   _____

9. par + _____ + chute =   _____

10. in + _____ + duce =   _____

11. be + _____ + ning =   _____

12. e + _____ + tric =   _____

13. Sep + _____ + ber =   _____

14. pun + _____ + ment =   _____

15. fa + _____ + ite =   _____

Colour in your score

Test 14

Test 15 Using dictionaries

You can use a **dictionary** to check the **spelling** of words.

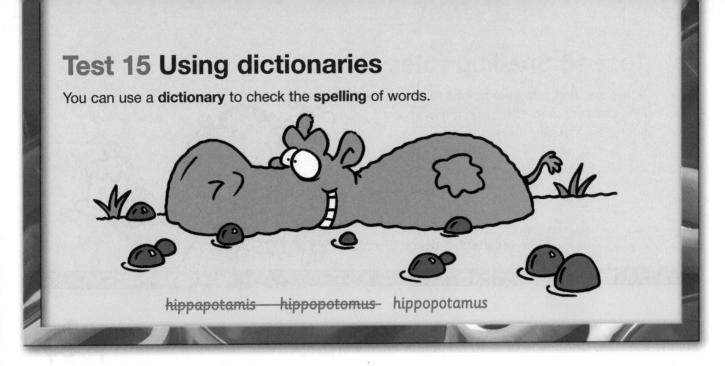

hippapotamis   hippopotomus   hippopotamus

Each of the following words is spelt incorrectly.
Write each word correctly. Use a dictionary if necessary.

1.   ocasion   _____

2.   priviledge   _____

3.   fasinate   _____

4.   exitement   _____

5.   immidiate   _____

6.   reconise   _____

7.   mathmatics   _____

8.   dissappear   _____

9.   controll   _____

10. marrage   _____

11. rubarb   _____

12. temporey   _____

13. disasterous   _____

14. sissors   _____

15. enviroment   _____

Colour in your score

Test 15

Test 16 Spelling rules

Some **spelling rules** are helpful to remember.
One common rule is: **i** (when it makes the
sound **ee**) before **e** except after **c**.

I received a piece of cake.

Follow the rule. Choose ie or ei to complete each word.

1. bel_____ve

2. rec_____ve

3. c_____ling

4. ch_____f

5. p_____ce

6. rel_____f

7. f_____ld

8. perc_____ve

9. dec_____ve

10. dec_____t

11. lad_____s

12. pr_____st

13. n_____ce

14. f_____rce

15. conc_____t

Colour in your score

Test 16

Test 17 Conditionals

A **conditional verb** tells you the action **might** happen (or might have happened), because it **depends** on someone or something else.

*I **would** buy an ice-cream if I had any money.*

Say if the conditional verbs in bold indicate the past or future tense.

1. If it stops raining we **might go** out. _____

2. If I had searched I **would have found** my watch. _____

3. She **would have passed** her test if she had tried harder. _____

4. I **might go** to America next year. _____

5. If I had heard the alarm I **would have got** up. _____

6. I **could have saved** my money but I didn't. _____

7. I **might play** cricket tomorrow. _____

8. If I were in charge I **would give** everyone a holiday. _____

9. If you won the Lottery what **would** you **buy**? _____

10. I **could have won** the race if I hadn't fallen over. _____

11. I **should have left** while I had the chance. _____

12. No one **would notice** if you went later. _____

13. How much **would** it **cost** to buy that dress? _____

14. I **would have read** the book if you hadn't disturbed me. _____

15. If you come to town with me I **might buy** you a present. _____

Colour in your score

15 14 13 12 11 10 9 8 7 6 5 4 3 2 1

Test 17

Test 18 Shortening words

When we write notes we can **abbreviate** some words.

I come from the USA.

USA = United States of America

Match up each abbreviation with its meaning.

1.	kph	United Nations
2.	dept	note well
3.	PTO	Crescent
4.	UN	kilometres per hour
5.	Rd	Her (or His) Royal Highness
6.	anon	please reply
7.	etc	Member of Parliament
8.	NB	department
9.	RSVP	Road
10.	BC	please turn over
11.	Sq	Before Christ
12.	Cresc	United Kingdom
13.	MP	anonymous
14.	UK	Square
15.	HRH	etcetera

Colour in your score

Test 18

Test 19 Our changing language

Our language is **changing** all the time. Words **fall out of use** and **new words** enter our language.

A **cobbler** made shoes.
We no longer use this word much.

An **astronaut** flies in space.
This is a new space-age word.

Match up these old words with their meanings.

1.	frock	hat
2.	quaff	drinking cup
3.	bonnet	dress
4.	satchel	container for coal
5.	guinea	drink
6.	tinker	an old coin
7.	goblet	schoolbag
8.	scuttle	a man who mended pots

Complete these new 'computer' words.

9. mon___ ___or

10. m___ ___em

11. key___ ___ ___rd

12. e-m___ ___ ___

13. ___ous___

14. inter___ ___ ___

15. w___bs___ ___ ___

15
14
13
12
11
10
9
8
7
6
5
4
3
2
1

Colour in your score

Test 19

Test 20 **Formal language**

THIEVES WILL BE PROSECUTED.

We speak to each other **informally**.   **Official language** is more **formal**.

Match up the formal words or phrases with their informal meanings.

1. forename   capital letters

2. marital status   the work you do

3. block letters   drinks

4. nationality   on the back

5. occupation   first name

6. I beg your pardon.   No smoking

7. Entrance forbidden!   whether you are married or single

8. duplicate   pay

9. beverages   what country you come from

10. consume   sorry

11. on the reverse   eat

12. remuneration   attach

13. dwelling   You are not allowed in.

14. Smoking prohibited!   where you live

15. append   a copy

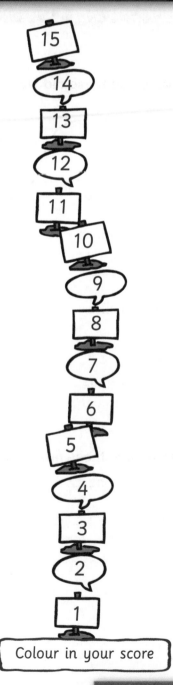

Colour in your score

Test 20

Test 21 Changing words

We can often change a **root word** by adding a **prefix**.

We can often change a **root word** by adding a **suffix**.

discomfort ← comfort → comfortable
(root word + prefix) (root word) (root word + suffix)

Choose the correct prefix to complete each word.

1. _____board (a/be)

2. _____loved (a/be)

3. _____mature (in/im)

4. _____considerate (in/im)

5. _____legible (ir/il)

6. _____responsible (ir/il)

7. _____noculars (bi/tri)

8. _____dent (bi/tri)

Work out the root word of each of these words.

9. accidentally _____

10. clumsily _____

11. suspicious _____

12. angry _____

13. circular _____

14. metallic _____

15. sensible _____

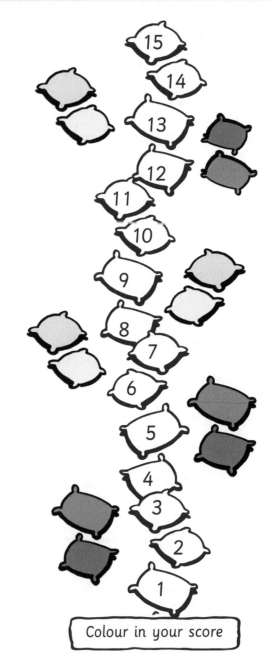

Colour in your score

Test 22 More about complex sentences

A **complex sentence** contains a **main clause** and a **subordinate** (less important) **clause**. The subordinate clause may not make sense on its own.

The detective arrested the man   who had robbed the bank.

main clause   subordinate clause

Join up each main clause with a sensible subordinate clause.

1. The children started talking   although I watered them.

2. Tom's mum was cross   because the gate was open.

3. The flowers did not grow   where I saw huge skyscrapers.

4. I visited New York   when the teacher went out.

5. The dog escaped   which I had lost.

6. It often rains   when she saw his messy bedroom.

7. I found the key   so I always carry an umbrella.

Now try these.

8. I had a bath   before she left.

9. The audience cheered   because it was starving.

10. My aunt hugged me   who is very naughty.

11. The lady asked the way   because I was so muddy.

12. Abdi is the boy   when she got lost.

13. Mrs Cane won the Lottery   before it got dark.

14. The child ran home   when the band played.

15. The dog ate hungrily   so she bought a new house.

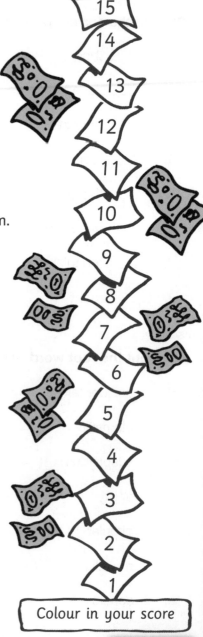

Colour in your score

Test 22

Test 23 Phrases and clauses

A **clause** may be used either as a **whole sentence** or as **part of a sentence**. A clause always contains a verb.

A **phrase** does **not** contain a **verb**. A phrase does **not make sense** on its own.

The balloon popped
clause

with a loud bang.
phrase

Write whether each of these is a clause or a phrase.

1. Sarah slipped over. _____

2. in a muddy puddle _____

3. after the programme _____

4. Sam rode her bike. _____

5. The spacecraft landed on the hill. _____

6. as fast as a flash _____

7. The lady put down her bag. _____

8. until next time _____

9. The lion pounced on the gazelle. _____

10. near the lake _____

11. until midnight _____

12. The baby smiled at me. _____

13. Some cars have big boots. _____

14. all green and slimy _____

15. A giraffe has a long neck. _____

Colour in your score

Test 24 More punctuation

It is important to check that your **punctuation** is correct.

Fill in the missing punctuation marks.

1. The monkeys were playing in the tree___

2. Amir bought eggs___ milk, bread and flour at the shop.

3. "Where do you live___" she asked.

4. "Get out___" he shouted.

5. The dog___s tail was wagging.

6. ___What book are you reading?" Shiraz asked.

7. After tea___ Mark watched TV.

8. Mrs Best said___ "Where is my bag?"

9. It isn___t a nice day.

10. The toy didn___t cost much.

11. "Come with me___ Ben," the teacher said.

12. "Stop that at once___" Mr Khan demanded.

13. The dog, a small poodle___ yapped loudly.

14. The door was open___ inviting him to enter.

15. "When I___ve got enough money, I'll retire," Mr Farr said.

Colour in your score

Test 24

Test 25 Another spelling rule

When a word has one vowel before a single final consonant, we double the consonant before adding a **suffix** – if the last syllable is stressed.

begin – beginning

Add the suffix ing. Write the word you make.

1.   rebel   _____

2.   admit   _____

3.   forget   _____

4.   prefer   _____

5.   signal   _____

Add the suffix ed. Write the word you make.

6.   regret   _____

7.   transmit   _____

8.   travel   _____

9.   occur   _____

10. control   _____

Take the suffix off. Write the root word you are left with.

11. fulfilled   _____

12. forbidding   _____

13. referred   _____

14. marvelled   _____

15. omitting   _____

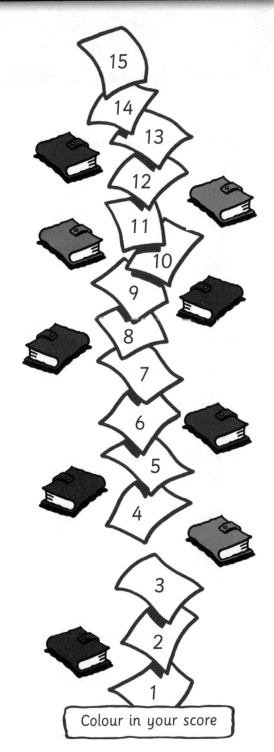

Colour in your score

Test 25

Test 26 Long and short vowels

ˇ
win
Short vowels make the
sound of the letter.

‾
wine
Long vowels say the
name of the letter.

Use the signs to show whether the vowels are long ‾ or short ˇ.

1. sigh

2. plush

3. truth

4. wild

5. swam

6. desk

7. show

8. shy

9. flip

10. drip

11. text

12. stay

13. most

14. blind

15. lost

Colour in your score

Test 27 Common word endings

It is helpful to learn the spelling of **common word endings**.

treasure　　　　　　　*colour*

Choose **our** or **ure** to complete each word.

1.　flav_____　　　　9.　lab_____

2.　cult_____　　　　10.　col_____

3.　furnit_____　　　11.　fig_____

4.　fav_____　　　　12.　fail_____

5.　mixt_____　　　　13.　vig_____

6.　hon_____　　　　14.　harb_____

7.　vap_____　　　　15.　capt_____

8.　inj_____

Colour in your score

Test 28 More common word endings

It is helpful to learn the spelling of **common word endings**.

nurs**ery** laborat**ory** di**ary**

Each of these words is spelt incorrectly. Spell each word correctly.

1. machinary   _____

2. factery   _____

3. delivory   _____

4. dictionery   _____

5. obscrvatery   _____

6. discovary   _____

7. granery   _____

8. laboratary   _____

9. jewellory   _____

10. dormitery   _____

11. flattary   _____

12. estuory   _____

13. militery   _____

14. territery   _____

15. librory   _____

Colour in your score

Test 28

Test 29 Similes

A **simile** is when one thing is compared to another. We often use the word **as** in similes.

Shh!

The children were **as** quiet **as** mice.

Complete these well-known similes with these words.

tortoise	swan	bat	fox	ox	mule	lion	elephant

1. as blind as a ＿＿＿＿＿＿

2. as obstinate as a ＿＿＿＿＿＿

3. as crafty as a ＿＿＿＿＿＿

4. as heavy as an ＿＿＿＿＿＿

5. as fierce as a ＿＿＿＿＿＿

6. as strong as an ＿＿＿＿＿＿

7. as graceful as a ＿＿＿＿＿＿

8. as slow as a ＿＿＿＿＿＿

Now do these.

thin	regular	fit	easy	safe	flat	sour

9. as ＿＿＿＿＿＿ as a fiddle

10. as ＿＿＿＿＿＿ as vinegar

11. as ＿＿＿＿＿＿ as a pancake

12. as ＿＿＿＿＿＿ as a rake

13. as ＿＿＿＿＿＿ as clockwork

14. as ＿＿＿＿＿＿ as ABC

15. as ＿＿＿＿＿＿ as a bank

15
14
13
12
11
10
9
8
7
6
5
4
3
2
1

Colour in your score

Test 30 Word games

We can learn a lot by playing **word games**.
They can help us with our **spelling** and
help to **improve our vocabulary**.

Use a dictionary to help you work out these clues.

These words all begin with she.

1. a law officer _____

2. a place for protection _____

3. very steep _____

4. large scissors _____

These words all begin with go.

5. a hairy berry _____

6. a prickly shrub _____

7. glasses for protection _____

8. a young goose _____

These words all begin with pea.

9. quiet _____

10. a bird with beautiful feathers _____

11. a kind of fuel _____

12. grows in a pod underground _____

These words all begin with ant.

13. old and valuable _____

14. an animal like a deer _____

15. kind of aerial _____

15

14

13

12

11

10

9

8

7

6

5

4

3

2

1

Colour in your score

Test 30

ANSWERS

Test 1
The missing vowels are in **bold**.
1. diamond
2. accidental
3. entrance
4. different
5. deodorant
6. mystery
7. cruel
8. interesting
9. effort
10. monastery
11. luncheon
12. separate
13. button
14. skeleton
15. photographer

Test 2
1. friend
2. assist
3. metre
4. able
5. beg
6. engine
7. change
8. king
9. bright
10. perfect
11. fix
12. serve
13. man
14. duck
15. hold

Test 3
1. I had my favourite meal – spaghetti.
2. I love apples – Ben hates them!
3. One boy looked strange – he was wearing a mask.
4. I won a prize – for coming first in spelling.
5. My uncle appeared – laughing as usual.
6. Christopher Wren built a famous cathedral – St Paul's.
7. Mr Smith has a sports car – a silver one.
8. I love music – especially pop music.
9. On the sand I found something interesting – an old chest.
10. Work hard – or you will never get a good job!
11. I know someone very brave – my friend Sarah.
12. Tom collects insects – especially beetles.
13. Mount Pico is in the Azores – a group of islands.
14. I saw a good programme last night – a monster film.
15. My room overlooks a wood – a small dark wood.

Test 4
1. door
2. man
3. wind
4. children
5. car
6. ride
7. ate
8. will try
9. cooked
10. cross
11. slippery
12. rough
13. colourful
14. scary
15. favourite

Test 5
1. nevertheless
2. or
3. because
4. as
5. before
6. when
7. so that
8. if
9. then
10. in case
11. until
12. however
13. but
14. as soon as
15. because

Test 6
Answers 1–8: the correct prefix is in **bold**.
1. **auto**graph
2. **il**legal
3. **de**port
4. **im**patient
5. **dis**approve
6. **mis**behave
7. **em**bark
8. **pre**arrange
9. confidence
10. bakery
11. communication
12. student
13. replacement
14. service
15. friendliness

Test 7
1. active
2. passive
3. active
4. passive
5. passive
6. active
7. active
8. passive
9. active
10. passive
11. active
12. active
13. passive
14. passive
15. active

Test 8
1. ballerina
2. piano
3. spaghetti
4. opera
5. confetti
6. buffet
7. cabaret
8. bracket
9. bouquet
10. duvet
11. skipper
12. sketch
13. schooner
14. smuggle
15. landscape

Test 9
1. knowledge
2. believe
3. mathematics
4. piece
5. ambitious
6. chocolate
7. business
8. government
9. separate
10. breadth
11. conscience
12. whole
13. island
14. cereal
15. soldier

Test 10
The missing punctuation marks are in **bold**.
1. Dr Turner's car was green.
2. Mrs Brown, who was getting angry, shouted loudly.
3. "Don't cross the busy road," Mrs Smith warned Tom.
4. Do you like oranges or lemons best?
5. During the night, it rained heavily.
6. "Where's my dinner?" the giant roared.
7. "I hate sprouts!" Sam shouted.
8. My brother hates music – but I love it.
9. In my pocket I had a coin, a sweet, a tissue and a badge.
10. The teachers' room is next to the office.
11. Where are you going?
12. I'm nearly eleven.
13. The film doesn't begin for an hour.
14. "Hands up!" the robber shouted.
15. "My job can be dangerous," the police officer said.

Test 11
1. signal
2. signature
3. design
4. liberty
5. liberal
6. liberate
7. audience
8. audible
9. auditorium
10. script
11. describe
12. scribble
13. spectator
14. spectacles
15. spectacular

Test 12
1. 1
2. 1
3. 2
4. 2
5. 1
6. 1
7. 2
8. 2
9. 2
10. 1
11. 2
12. 2
13. 2
14. 2
15. 1

Test 13
1. grow fonder
2. choosers
3. than words
4. flock together
5. twice shy
6. a silver lining
7. spoil the broth
8. in one basket
9. less speed
10. the sun shines
11. than one
12. never
13. you leap
14. out of mind
15. saves nine

Test 14
The missing second syllable is in **bold**.
1. de**ter**mine
2. **u**niform
3. hos**pi**tal
4. **ex**cellent
5. at**ten**tion
6. **dif**ferent
7. ad**ven**ture
8. syl**lab**le
9. **par**achute
10. **in**troduce
11. be**gin**ning
12. e**lec**tric
13. Sep**tem**ber
14. **pun**ishment
15. **fa**vourite

Test 15
1. occasion
2. privilege
3. fascinate
4. excitement
5. immediate
6. recognise
7. mathematics
8. disappear
9. control
10. marriage
11. rhubarb
12. temporary
13. disastrous
14. scissors
15. environment

Test 16

The missing **ie** or **ei** are in **bold**.

1. bel**ie**ve
2. rec**ei**ve
3. c**ei**ling
4. ch**ie**f
5. p**ie**ce
6. rel**ie**f
7. f**ie**ld
8. perc**ei**ve
9. dec**ei**ve
10. dec**ei**t
11. lad**ie**s
12. pr**ie**st
13. n**ie**ce
14. f**ie**rce
15. conc**ei**t

Test 17

1. future
2. past
3. past
4. future
5. past
6. past
7. future
8. future
9. future
10. past
11. past
12. future
13. future
14. past
15. future

Test 18

1. kilometres per hour
2. department
3. please turn over
4. United Nations
5. Road
6. anonymous
7. etcetera
8. note well
9. please reply
10. Before Christ
11. Square
12. Crescent
13. Member of Parliament
14. United Kingdom
15. Her (or His) Royal Highness

Test 19

1. dress
2. drink
3. hat
4. schoolbag
5. an old coin
6. a man who mended pots
7. drinking cup
8. container for coal
9. monitor
10. modem
11. keyboard
12. e-mail
13. mouse
14. internet
15. website

Test 20

1. first name
2. whether you are married or single
3. capital letters
4. what country you come from
5. the work you do
6. sorry
7. You are not allowed in.
8. a copy
9. drinks
10. eat
11. on the back
12. pay
13. where you live
14. No smoking
15. attach

Test 21

Answers 1-8: the correct prefix is in **bold**.

1. **a**board
2. **be**loved
3. **im**mature
4. **in**considerate
5. **il**legible
6. **ir**responsible
7. **bin**oculars
8. **tri**dent
9. accident
10. clumsy
11. suspicion
12. anger
13. circle
14. metal
15. sense

Test 22

1. when the teacher went out.
2. when she saw his messy bedroom.
3. although I watered them.
4. where I saw huge skyscrapers.
5. because the gate was open.
6. so I always carry an umbrella.
7. which I had lost.
8. because I was so muddy.
9. when the band played.
10. before she left.
11. when she got lost.
12. who is very naughty.
13. so she bought a new house.
14. before it got dark.
15. because it was starving.

Test 23

1. clause
2. phrase
3. phrase
4. clause
5. clause
6. phrase
7. clause
8. phrase
9. clause
10. phrase
11. phrase
12. clause
13. clause
14. phrase
15. clause

Test 24

The missing punctuation marks are in **bold**.

1. The monkeys were playing in the tree**.**
2. Amir bought eggs**,** milk**,** bread and flour at the shop**.**
3. **"**Where do you live**?"** she asked.
4. **"**Get out**!"** he shouted.
5. The dog**'**s tail was wagging.
6. **"**What book are you reading**?"** Shiraz asked.
7. After tea**,** Mark watched TV.
8. Mrs Best said**,** **"**Where is my bag**?"**
9. It isn**'**t a nice day.
10. The toy didn**'**t cost much.
11. **"**Come with me**,** Ben**,"** the teacher said.
12. **"**Stop that at once**!"** Mr Khan demanded.
13. The dog**,** a small poodle**,** yapped loudly.
14. The door was open**,** inviting him to enter.
15. **"**When I**'**ve got enough money**,** I**'**ll retire**,"** Mr Farr said.

Test 25

1. rebelling
2. admitting
3. forgetting
4. preferring
5. signalling
6. regretted
7. transmitted
8. travelled
9. occurred
10. controlled
11. fulfil
12. forbid
13. refer
14. marvel
15. omit

Test 26

1. sĭgh
2. plŭsh
3. trū th
4. wīld
5. swăm
6. dĕsk
7. shōw
8. shȳ
9. flĭp
10. drĭp
11. tĕxt
12. stāy
13. mōst
14. blīnd
15. lŏst

Test 27

The missing **our** or **ure** are in **bold**.

1. flav**our**
2. cult**ure**
3. furnit**ure**
4. fav**our**
5. mixt**ure**
6. hon**our**
7. vap**our**
8. inj**ure**
9. lab**our**
10. col**our**
11. fig**ure**
12. fail**ure**
13. vig**our**
14. harb**our**
15. capt**ure**

Test 28

The correct spellings are in **bold**.

1. machin**ery**
2. fact**ory**
3. deliv**ery**
4. diction**ary**
5. observat**ory**
6. discov**ery**
7. gran**ary**
8. laborat**ory**
9. jewell**ery**
10. dormit**ory**
11. flatt**ery**
12. estu**ary**
13. milit**ary**
14. territ**ory**
15. libr**ary**

Test 29

1. bat
2. mule
3. fox
4. elephant
5. lion
6. ox
7. swan
8. tortoise
9. fit
10. sour
11. flat
12. thin
13. regular
14. easy
15. safe

Test 30

1. sheriff
2. shelter
3. sheer
4. shears
5. gooseberry
6. gorse
7. goggles
8. gosling
9. peaceful
10. peacock
11. peat
12. peanut
13. antique
14. antelope
15. antenna

Make it easy...

Maths

with Quick Tests

Age 10-11

Place value

To **multiply** by 100, move all the digits two places to the left.

To **multiply** by 1000, move all the digits three places to the left.

To **divide** by 100, move all the digits two places to the right.

To **divide** by 1000 move all the digits three places to the right.

			3	6	.	4
	3	6	4	0	.	
3	6	4	0	0	.	

4	1	3	0	.		
		4	1	.	3	0
			4	.	1	3	0

I

Multiply each of these by 100.

a 745 → ☐

5610 → ☐

8.65 → ☐

298 → ☐

3114 → ☐

21.8 → ☐

Divide each of these by 100.

c 4800 → ☐

27 300 → ☐

4910 → ☐

62 100 → ☐

38 000 → ☐

3158 → ☐

Multiply each of these by 1000.

b 26 → ☐

968 → ☐

6.05 → ☐

0.003 → ☐

314 → ☐

2317 → ☐

19.8 → ☐

1.65 → ☐

Divide each of these by 1000.

d 294 000 → ☐

6 148 000 → ☐

81 500 → ☐

62 → ☐

817 000 → ☐

1 722 000 → ☐

13 100 → ☐

40 → ☐

II

Write the missing numbers.

a $48 \times$ ◯ $= 4800$

b ◯ $\times 1000 = 570$

c $387 \div 100 =$ ◯

d ◯ $\div 100 = 0.06$

e $61.3 \times$ ◯ $= 61300$

f ◯ $\div 1000 = 8.5$

g $0.07 \times$ ◯ $= 7$

h ◯ $\div 10 = 16.05$

i ◯ $\times 100 = 9413$

2

Number sequences

Look at the difference between numbers in a sequence.

This can show the **pattern** or **rule**.

17 20 23 26 ...		9 4 −1 −6 ...

The rule is +3

The rule is −5

I Continue these sequences and write the rules.

a
| 7 | 11 | 15 | 19 | | | |

Rule: _____

b
| 23 | 15 | 7 | −1 | | | |

Rule: _____

c
| 7.5 | 9 | 10.5 | 12 | | | |

Rule: _____

Write the missing numbers in these sequences.

d
| 6 | | 28 | 39 | | |

e
| 0.9 | 0.89 | | | 0.86 | |

f
| 55 | 40 | | | | −20 |

g
| 37 | | | | 73 | 82 |

h
| 0.25 | 0.5 | | | | 1.5 |

i
| | | −63 | −44 | −25 | |

II Continue these sequences of special numbers. Describe the rule for each sequence.

a 1   4   9   16   ☐ ☐ ☐ ☐

_____

b 1   3   6   10   ☐ ☐ ☐ ☐

_____

c 1   2   4   8   ☐ ☐ ☐ ☐

_____

Decimals

A decimal point **separates** units from tenths.

tens	units		tenths	hundredths	thousandths
1	7	•	8	3	5

In seventeen point eight three five, the value of the digit 3 is
3 hundredths or → $\frac{3}{100}$

I Complete these.

Write the value of the red digit.

a 87.384 → [ ]

d 117.805 → [ ]

b 4.006 → [ ]

e 3.068 → [ ]

c 13.45 → [ ]

f 20.309 → [ ]

Continue these patterns for two more numbers.

g | 1.96 | → | 1.97 | → | 1.98 | → | | → | |

h | 3.018 | → | 3.019 | → | 3.02 | → | | → | |

i | 4.947 | → | 4.948 | → | 4.949 | → | | → | |

j | 0.998 | → | 0.999 | → | 1.0 | → | | → | |

II Rearrange each set to make a decimal number as near as possible to 1. There must be one number in front of the decimal point e.g. 6.401.

a

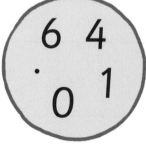

b

c

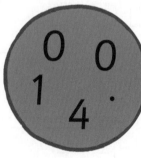

d

[ ]   [ ]   [ ]   [ ]

Multiples

Multiples are numbers made by **multiplying together** two numbers.

12, 90, 240 and 3000 are all multiples of 3. These numbers are divisible by 3.

Learn and use these rules of divisibility.

A whole number is a multiple of:

2 if the last digit is even e.g. 752

3 if the sum of its digits can be divided by 3 e.g. 132 (1 + 3 + 2 = 6)

4 if the last two digits can be divided by 4 e.g. 528 (28 is divisible by 4)

5 if the last digit is 5 or 0

6 if it is even and divisible by 3, e.g. 156

10 if the last digit is 0

I Look at these numbers.

| 296 | 4120 | 930 | 2004 | 825 | 726 |

a Which numbers are multiples of 3? _____

b Which numbers are divisible by 4? _____

c Which number is a multiple of both 4 and 6? _____

d Which numbers are divisible by both 3 and 5? _____

e Write each of the numbers on the Venn diagram.

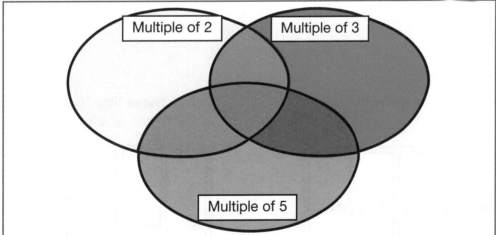

II 504 is divisible by many numbers. Answer these.

a Tick the numbers below that 504 is exactly divisible by.

2 ☐   3 ☐   4 ☐   5 ☐   6 ☐   7 ☐   8 ☐   9 ☐   10 ☐

b Find another number that is divisible by more than six of these numbers. ☐

c What is the smallest number that is divisible by 2, 3, 4 and 5? ☐

Ratio

Ratios are used to **compare the number of parts** that make up a whole quantity.

In this flower border there are two tulips for every one daffodil.

The ratio of daffodils to tulips is 1 for every 2, written as 1:2.

I **Write the ratio of rectangle to square bricks for each garden path design.**

a Ratio ☐

b Ratio ☐

c Ratio ☐

d If 48 square bricks are used for each design, how many rectangle bricks are needed for each?

Design a ☐

Design b ☐

Design c ☐

II Colour these tiles to show the ratio of red to blue tiles as 1:3.

Colour these tiles to show the ratio of green to yellow tiles as 1:4.

a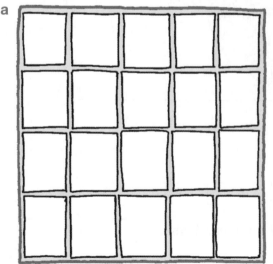

b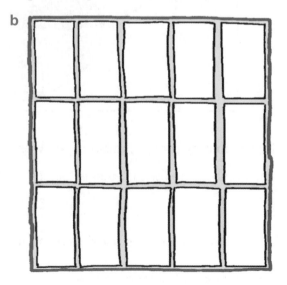

Quadrilaterals

Shapes with four straight sides are called quadrilaterals.

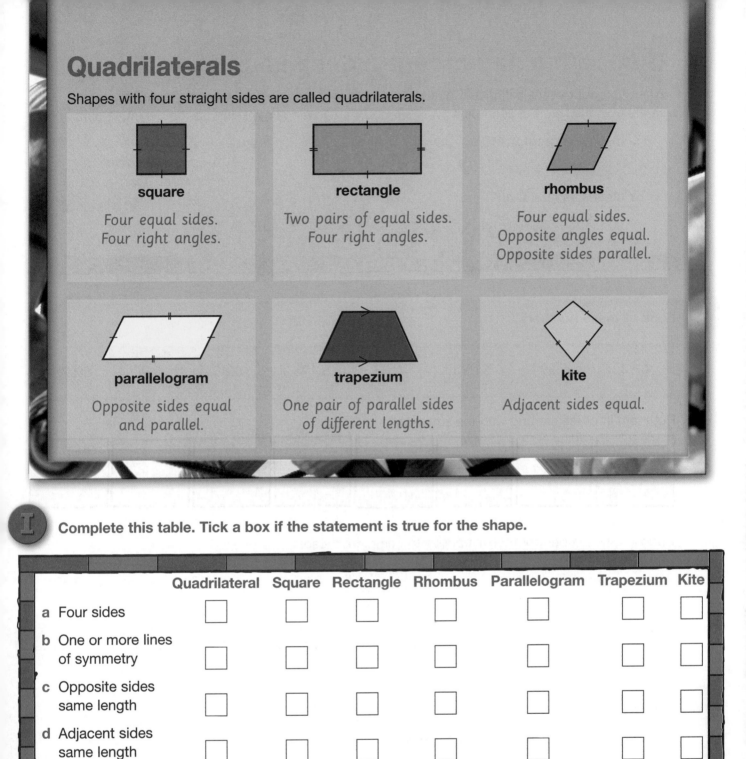

square
Four equal sides.
Four right angles.

rectangle
Two pairs of equal sides.
Four right angles.

rhombus
Four equal sides.
Opposite angles equal.
Opposite sides parallel.

parallelogram
Opposite sides equal
and parallel.

trapezium
One pair of parallel sides
of different lengths.

kite
Adjacent sides equal.

1 Complete this table. Tick a box if the statement is true for the shape.

	Quadrilateral	Square	Rectangle	Rhombus	Parallelogram	Trapezium	Kite
a Four sides	☐	☐	☐	☐	☐	☐	☐
b One or more lines of symmetry	☐	☐	☐	☐	☐	☐	☐
c Opposite sides same length	☐	☐	☐	☐	☐	☐	☐
d Adjacent sides same length	☐	☐	☐	☐	☐	☐	☐
e Both pairs of opposite sides parallel	☐	☐	☐	☐	☐	☐	☐
f One or more right angles	☐	☐	☐	☐	☐	☐	☐

2 Draw two different quadrilaterals on the grid with a ruler.

They must each have the following:

- fewer than 2 right angles
- opposite sides equal
- opposite sides parallel.

7

Comparing and ordering decimals

When you put decimals in order, look carefully at the value of each digit.

It may help to write the numbers in a column lining up the decimal point.

> means 'is greater than'

4.85 > 4.588

< means 'is less than'

3.07 < 3.71

```
1 0 . 6 5
    8 . 9
    8 . 7 2
    8 . 0 5 5
```

Compare each column, starting from the left.

I Look at these numbers.

| 6.93 | 6.59 | 6.095 | 6.05 | 6.198 | 6.85 | 6.9 | 6.625 |

a Put them in order, starting with the smallest.

Choose any number from the list above to complete these.

b 7.04 > [   ] > 6.92

c 6.9 > [   ] > 6.63

d 6.79 < [   ] < 6.89

e [   ] < 6.82 < [   ]

f [   ] > 6.4 > [   ]

g [   ] < 6.19 < [   ]

II Now try this.

Use the digits 1, 2, 6, 9 and a decimal point.

[ ] . [ ] [ ] [ ]

a Make six numbers between 0 and 2. Write them in order, starting with the smallest.

b Make six numbers between 9 and 10. Write them in order, starting with the smallest.

Use this area to show your working out.

Mental addition and subtraction

Use mental methods to **add** and **subtract**.

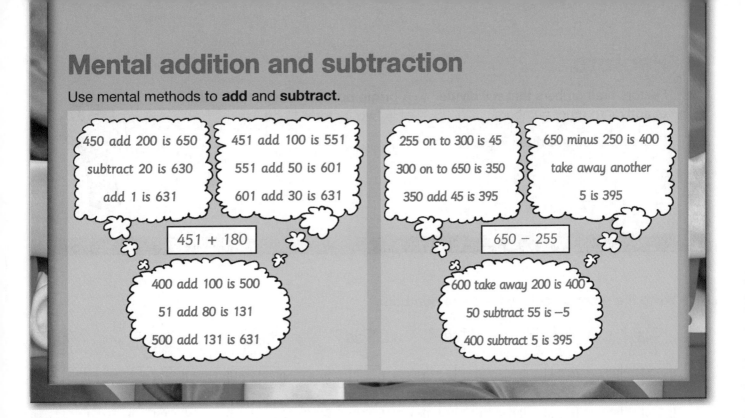

450 add 200 is 650
subtract 20 is 630
add 1 is 631

451 add 100 is 551
551 add 50 is 601
601 add 30 is 631

451 + 180

400 add 100 is 500
51 add 80 is 131
500 add 131 is 631

255 on to 300 is 45
300 on to 650 is 350
350 add 45 is 395

650 minus 250 is 400
take away another
5 is 395

650 − 255

600 take away 200 is 400
50 subtract 55 is −5
400 subtract 5 is 395

Complete these addition squares. Add the rows and columns to find the totals.

Work out the differences between these pairs of numbers.

a
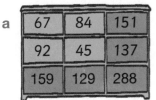
67	84	151
92	45	137
159	129	288

d
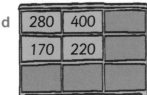
280	400	
170	220	

g
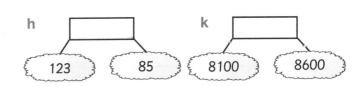
93   109

j
345   910

b
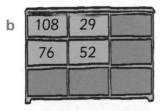
108	29	
76	52	

e
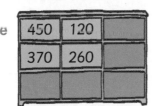
450	120	
370	260	

h
123   85

k
8100   8600

c
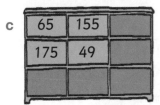
65	155	
175	49	

f
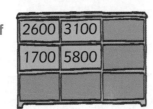
2600	3100	
1700	5800	

i
240   185

l
2400   7950

5, 6 and 7 are consecutive numbers. Find three consecutive numbers to make each of these totals.

a [ ] + [ ] + [ ] = 57

d [ ] + [ ] + [ ] = 504

b [ ] + [ ] + [ ] = 81

e [ ] + [ ] + [ ] = 96

c [ ] + [ ] + [ ] = 339

f [ ] + [ ] + [ ] = 273

Factors

Factors are numbers that will **divide exactly** into other numbers.

Factors are often written in pairs.

Factors of 24

(1, 24) (2, 12) (3, 8) (4, 6)

A **prime number** is a number with only two factors: 1 and itself.

7, 23, 29... are all prime numbers.

No other number divides exactly into these.

 Write the pairs of factors for these numbers.

a 45   b 18   c 63   d 30   e 42   f 40   g 48

(⬚ , ⬚) (⬚ , ⬚) (⬚ , ⬚) (⬚ , ⬚) (⬚ , ⬚) (⬚ , ⬚) (⬚ , ⬚)

(⬚ , ⬚) (⬚ , ⬚) (⬚ , ⬚) (⬚ , ⬚) (⬚ , ⬚) (⬚ , ⬚) (⬚ , ⬚)

(⬚ , ⬚) (⬚ , ⬚) (⬚ , ⬚) (⬚ , ⬚) (⬚ , ⬚) (⬚ , ⬚) (⬚ , ⬚)

(⬚ , ⬚) (⬚ , ⬚) (⬚ , ⬚) (⬚ , ⬚)

(⬚ , ⬚)

Write the factors for these square numbers in order.

h 25 ➞ [⬚]   i 49 ➞ [⬚]   j 64 ➞ [⬚]

k What do you notice about the number of factors of square numbers?

_____

II Write the numbers 1 to 36 on this Venn diagram.

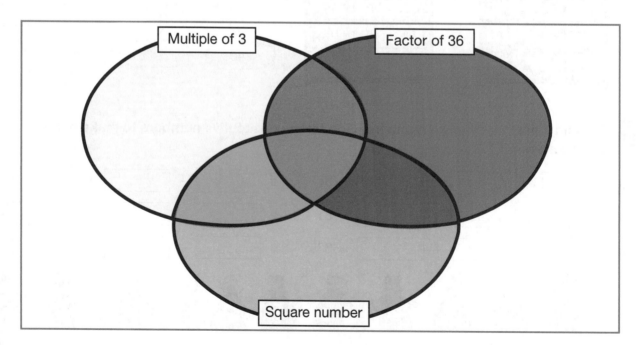

Multiplication and division facts

To help learn division facts, use the related multiplication facts.

This trio makes the following facts:

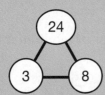

$3 \times 8 = 24$

$8 \times 3 = 24$

$24 \div 3 = 8$

$24 \div 8 = 3$

I Complete these.

a $9 \times 3 = \boxed{}$

$\boxed{} \div 3 = 9$

$\boxed{} \div 9 = 3$

c $4 \times 7 = \boxed{}$

$\boxed{} \div 4 = 7$

$\boxed{} \div 7 = 4$

e $6 \times 9 = \boxed{}$

$\boxed{} \div 6 = 9$

$\boxed{} \div 9 = 6$

b $7 \times 8 = \boxed{}$

$\boxed{} \div 8 = 7$

$\boxed{} \div 7 = 8$

d $8 \times 6 = \boxed{}$

$\boxed{} \div 8 = 6$

$\boxed{} \div 6 = 8$

f $5 \times 9 = \boxed{}$

$\boxed{} \div 5 = 9$

$\boxed{} \div 9 = 5$

Write the missing numbers for these multiplication grids.

g

x	7	8	4
6	42		
9			
		40	

h

x	6		5
	48		
			35
9		27	

i

x			
	56	42	21
	40	30	15
	72	54	27

II Answer these as quickly as you can. Write the answers on a separate piece of paper, so you can try to beat your best time.

a $48 \div 6$

$90 \div 10$

$54 \div 9$

$64 \div 8$

$35 \div 5$

$36 \div 6$

b $18 \div 3$

$36 \div 4$

$27 \div 3$

$80 \div 8$

$32 \div 4$

$15 \div 5$

c $81 \div 9$

$45 \div 5$

$63 \div 7$

$49 \div 7$

$32 \div 8$

$16 \div 4$

d $72 \div 9$

$21 \div 3$

$60 \div 10$

$30 \div 5$

$48 \div 8$

$28 \div 4$

Fractions

In a fraction, the denominator shows how many parts an amount is divided into and the numerator shows how many of these parts to include.

$\frac{4}{5} \rightarrow$ numerator
$\phantom{\frac{4}{5}} \rightarrow$ denominator

Equivalent fractions are worth the same.

$$\frac{4}{5} = \frac{12}{15}$$

To simplify fractions, use a factor of the **numerator** and **denominator** to divide.

$$\frac{12}{15} \div 3 = \frac{4}{5}$$

 Simplify these fractions.

a $\dfrac{6}{10} \div \square = \dfrac{\square}{\square}$

b $\dfrac{4}{12} \div \square = \dfrac{\square}{\square}$

c $\dfrac{10}{15} \div \square = \dfrac{\square}{\square}$

d $\dfrac{20}{24} \div \square = \dfrac{\square}{\square}$

e $\dfrac{30}{100} \div \square = \dfrac{\square}{\square}$

f $\dfrac{9}{24} \div \square = \dfrac{\square}{\square}$

g $\dfrac{18}{30} = \dfrac{\square}{\square}$

h $\dfrac{300}{500} = \dfrac{\square}{\square}$

i $\dfrac{18}{24} = \dfrac{\square}{\square}$

 Draw a line to join the matching pairs of fractions.

Addition

Before you add numbers, estimate an **approximate answer**.

17.8 + 29.6

↓

approximate answer

18 + 30

↓

48

If the numbers are too difficult to calculate mentally, you can use a written method.

```
   17.8
+ 29.6
 ------
  47.4
   1 1
```

Line up the decimal points and start adding from the right.

I Estimate each answer, then calculate using a written method.

a estimate

```
    31.6
+  92.54
```

c estimate

```
   46.51
+  39.74
```

e estimate

```
   174.6
+   38.9
```

g estimate

```
   358.2
+  147.9
```

b estimate

```
    4.29
+  17.68
```

d estimate

```
    3.07
+  68.19
```

f estimate

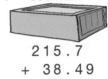

```
   215.7
+  38.49
```

h estimate

```
   491.6
+  87.95
```

II These vans can each carry a total of three crates. The total weight of the crates must be exactly 200 kg.

 80.59kg  60.59kg  85.17kg  62.57kg  76.84kg  34.24kg

Which crates does each van take?

Van A

☐ kg + ☐ kg + ☐ kg = 200 kg

Van B

☐ kg + ☐ kg + ☐ kg = 200 kg

Time

To solve time problems, count on along a time line.

Count on from the start time to the finish in easy steps.

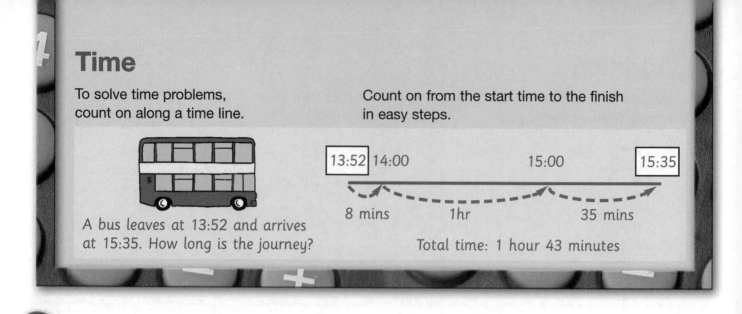

A bus leaves at 13:52 and arrives at 15:35. How long is the journey?

| 13:52 | 14:00 | 15:00 | 15:35 |

8 mins   1hr   35 mins

Total time: 1 hour 43 minutes

I   **Use the timetable to answer these questions.**

a What time does the 11:05 from Thorpe arrive in Salham?

_____

b How long does it take the 14:46 from Ashby to reach Welby?

_____

c What is the total journey time from Thorpe to Welby for train 4?

_____

d You arrive at Melton station for 2.50pm to catch a train to Salham. How many minutes will you wait for your train?

_____

e Which is the fastest train from Thorpe to Welby?

_____

f How long is the journey from Melton to Bilton on train 2?

_____

Timetable

Station	Train 1	Train 2	Train 3	Train 4
Thorpe	09:03	11:05	14:20	19:32
Ashby	09:28	11:31	14:46	19:59
Melton	09:50	12:02	15:15	20:30
Salham	10:13	12:27	15:39	20:53
Bilton	10:52	13:06	16:17	21:25
Welby	11:12	13:23	16:34	21:43

II   **Write your age in different ways. Remember leap years!**

| | years (part year as a fraction) |

| | months |

| | weeks |

| | days |

| | hours |

| | minutes |

| | seconds |

3-D shapes

Polyhedra are 3-D shapes made from a number of polygons. Each polyhedron has:

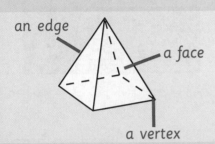

an edge

a face

a vertex

When a polyhedron is laid out flat, it makes the **net** of a shape.

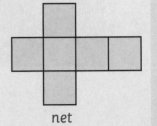

polyhedron   net

I   Write the name of the shape that each net makes.

a

_____

c
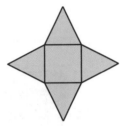
_____

e
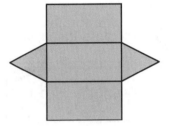
_____

b
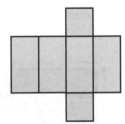
_____

d
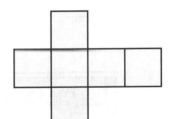
_____

f

_____

II   Complete this chart.

Shape		Number of faces	Number of edges	Number of vertices
cube		6	12	8
cuboid				
tetrahedron				
square-based pyramid				
pentagonal prism				
triangular prism				

Area and perimeter

The area of a rectangle is length x width.

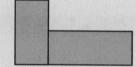

5 cm

3 cm

Area = 5 x 3 = 15 cm²

The perimeter of a rectangle is 2 x (length + width).

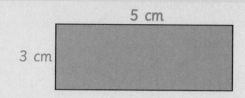

5 cm

3 cm

Perimeter = 5 + 5 + 3 + 3 = 16 cm

Some shapes can be split into rectangles.

I Calculate the area and perimeter of each garden plan.

a

8m
5m
9m
5m

Area =

Perimeter =

c

10m
6m
12m
4m
5m

Area =

Perimeter =

e

15m
6m
6m
2m
3m
3m

Area =

Perimeter =

b

20m
8m
6m
15m

Area =

Perimeter =

d

12m
5m
10m
10m

Area =

Perimeter =

f

7m
7m
4m
2m
5m

Area =

Perimeter =

II Find the area of each part of this garden.

a Area of pond →

b Area of paving →

c Area of grass →

d Area of whole garden →

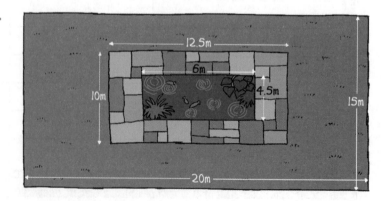

12.5m
6m
10m
4.5m
15m
20m

Averages

Mean, mode and median are all different types of average.

Mode: the number that appears most often. <u>3</u> <u>3</u> 4 7 8

Median: the middle number when listed in order. 3 3 <u>4</u> 7 8

Mean: add the numbers and divide the total by the number of items used.

$$\frac{8 + 7 + 4 + 3 + 3}{5} = 5$$

 This graph shows the height of nine children. Look at it, then answer the questions.

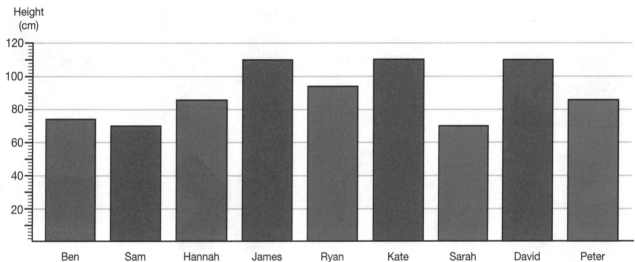

a Write the heights in order, starting with the tallest child.

b What is the height mode? _____

c What is the median height? _____

d What is the mean height of all the children? _____

These are the shoe sizes for the nine children.

a Calculate the average shoe size for the children.

Mode ➛ _____   Median ➛ _____   Mean ➛ _____

b What do you notice? _____

c Work out the average shoe size for your family or friends. _____

17

Symmetry

A line of symmetry is the same as a **mirror line**. One side of the line is the reflection of the other side.

I. Draw the lines of symmetry on each shape.

a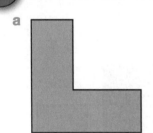

c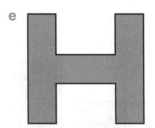

e

g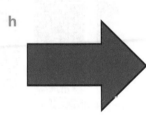

b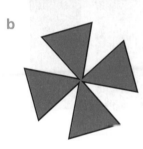

d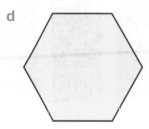

f

h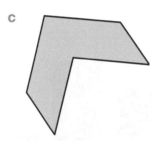

II. Draw the reflection of each shape.

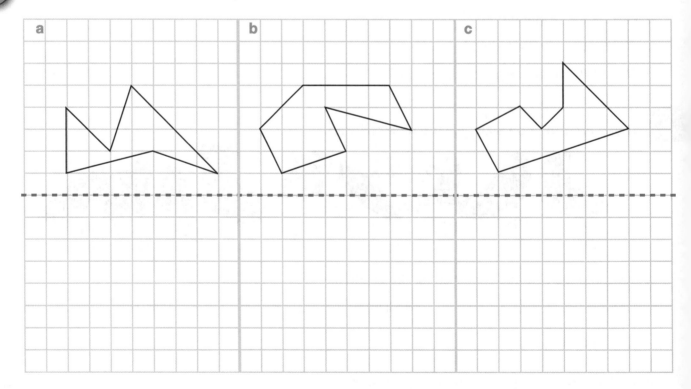

a b c

Measures problems

When you read a problem, try to 'picture' it in your head.

Think of the calculations that are needed to solve the problem.

Length	Mass	Capacity
1 cm = 10 mm	1 kg = 1000 g	1 l = 1000 ml
1 m = 100 cm	1 tonne = 1000 kg	1 cl = 10 ml
1 km = 1000 m		

$250 \ g = \frac{1}{4} \ kg$

$30 \ ml = 0.03 \ l$

Use decimals and fractions to show parts.

 Answer these problems.

a Kelly travels 42.84 kilometres by car and 1350 metres on foot.

How far does she travel altogether in kilometres? _____

How far does she travel altogether in metres? _____

b A full bucket holds 2.8 litres. A jug holds 0.4 litres.

How many jugs will fill the bucket? _____

c A piece of wood is 27.68 metres long. Five equal lengths are cut
from the wood, leaving a length of 3.68 metres.
What is the length of each of the five pieces? _____

d A bus travels 15.8 kilometres in one journey. The bus does the journey six times a day
Monday to Friday and four times a day on Saturday and Sunday.

How many kilometres does the bus travel in total in one week? _____

 Look at the speed of these bugs, then answer the questions.

Anty travelled 25 cm in 10 seconds.

Bill travelled 1.3 m in 1 minute.

Cecil travelled 500 mm in 30 seconds.

Dennis travelled 1.5 cm in 1 second.

a Who was the fastest bug? _____

b Who was the slowest bug? _____

Ordering fractions

To compare the size of fractions, you can change them so they have the same, or common, denominator.

Example

Which is bigger $\frac{3}{5}$ or $\frac{2}{3}$?

Use equivalent fractions to find a common denominator.

$\frac{3}{5} = \frac{9}{15}$

$\frac{2}{3} = \frac{10}{15}$

So $\frac{2}{3}$ is bigger than $\frac{3}{5}$.

I Draw a circle around the fractions that are less than $\frac{1}{2}$. Colour the fractions that are less than $\frac{1}{4}$.

a  $\frac{1}{3}$

c $\frac{1}{8}$

e $\frac{3}{5}$

g 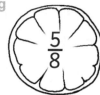 $\frac{5}{8}$

i $\frac{5}{9}$

b  $\frac{5}{12}$

d  $\frac{3}{10}$

f  $\frac{7}{8}$

h  $\frac{7}{10}$

j  $\frac{3}{20}$

II Put each set of fractions in order, starting with the smallest.

a $\frac{1}{2}$ $\frac{1}{5}$ $\frac{3}{10}$

b $\frac{2}{3}$ $\frac{3}{4}$ $\frac{7}{12}$

c $\frac{11}{12}$ $\frac{2}{3}$ $\frac{5}{6}$

d $\frac{7}{10}$ $\frac{11}{20}$ $\frac{4}{5}$

e $\frac{1}{3}$  $\frac{3}{8}$ $\frac{1}{4}$

f $\frac{5}{6}$ $\frac{7}{12}$ $\frac{1}{4}$

20

Handling data

Line graphs have points plotted that are joined with a line.

- Read up from the **horizontal axis** to meet the line or point.

- Read across to the **vertical axis** to give the value.

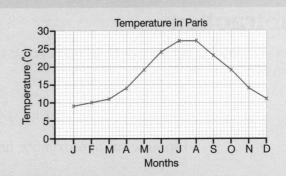

Temperature in Paris

These are conversion graphs for pints and gallons. The conversions are approximate.

a Complete the line graph for gallons.

| 1 litre = 1.75 pints |

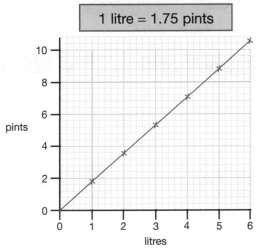

pints / litres

| 1 gallon = 4.5 litres |

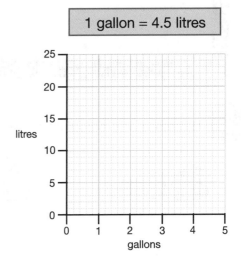

litres / gallons

Use the graphs to complete these.

b 8 pints = [   ] litres   d [   ] pints = 3.2 litres   f [   ] litres = 3 gallons

c 5 litres = [   ] pints   e 2 gallons = [   ] litres   g [   ] gallons = 22 litres

---

Temperature is measured in degrees using two scales: Fahrenheit (°F) and Celsius (°C). This graph converts °F to °C approximately. Use the graph to complete this chart.

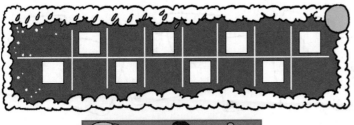

Graph to convert °F to °C

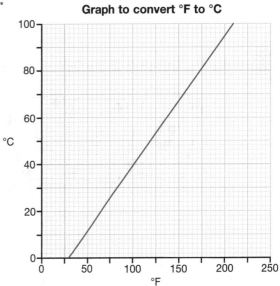

°C / °F

21

Subtraction

When you need to subtract decimal numbers, it may be too difficult to work out the answer mentally.

$$74.83 - 39.16$$

Estimate an approximate answer first. $75 - 40 = 35$

Try this written method.

$$
\begin{array}{r}
{}^6\!\!\diagup\!\!4^1.\,{}^7\!\!8^1 3 \\
-\ 39.16 \\
\hline
35.67
\end{array}
$$

Start from the right-hand column.

Take away the bottom number from the top.

If the top number is smaller, exchange a ten.

I Estimate and calculate each answer.

a estimate

$$
\begin{array}{r}
17.85 \\
-\ 9.93 \\
\hline
\end{array}
$$

c estimate

$$
\begin{array}{r}
73.92 \\
-\ 27.18 \\
\hline
\end{array}
$$

e estimate
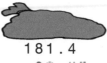

$$
\begin{array}{r}
181.4 \\
-\ 39.62 \\
\hline
\end{array}
$$

g estimate
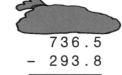

$$
\begin{array}{r}
736.5 \\
-\ 293.8 \\
\hline
\end{array}
$$

b estimate
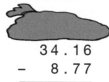

$$
\begin{array}{r}
34.16 \\
-\ 8.77 \\
\hline
\end{array}
$$

d estimate

$$
\begin{array}{r}
52.08 \\
-\ 16.14 \\
\hline
\end{array}
$$

f estimate

$$
\begin{array}{r}
372.1 \\
-\ 87.93 \\
\hline
\end{array}
$$

h estimate
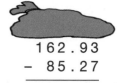

$$
\begin{array}{r}
162.93 \\
-\ 85.27 \\
\hline
\end{array}
$$

II Write the missing digits 0–9 in the spaces.

a
$$
\begin{array}{r}
3\ \square\ 1\,.\,6\ 9 \\
-\ \ 5\ 8\,.\,7\ 4 \\
\hline
2\ 7\ \square\,.\,9\ \square
\end{array}
$$

b
$$
\begin{array}{r}
2\ 7\ \square\,.\,9 \\
-1\ \square\ 6\,.\,7\ 1 \\
\hline
1\ 6\ 5\,.\,1\ 9
\end{array}
$$

c
$$
\begin{array}{r}
1\ 0\ \square\,.\,9 \\
-\ \ \square\ 8\,.\,7 \\
\hline
1\ 8\,.\,2
\end{array}
$$

d
$$
\begin{array}{r}
\square\ 6\ 4\,.\,8\ 2 \\
-2\ 1\ 5\,.\,\square \\
\hline
2\ 4\ \square\,.\,1\ 2
\end{array}
$$

Percentages

Percent means 'out of 100'. The sign is %.

Percentages are fractions out of 100.

To change scores to percentages, make them out of 100.

$8 \text{ out of } 10 = \frac{8}{10} = \frac{80}{100} = 80\%$

$10\% \text{ of } £12 \to \frac{1}{10} \text{ of } £12 = £1.20$

$20\% \text{ of } £12 \to \text{ double } 10\%$
$= £2.40$

$5\% \text{ of } £12 \to \text{ half } 10\% = 60p$

I Change these test scores to percentages.

a 6 out of 10 = ☐ %

b 15 out of 20 = ☐ %

c 18 out of 20 = ☐ %

d 21 out of 25 = ☐ %

e 2 out of 10 = ☐ %

f 24 out of 25 = ☐ %

g 30 out of 50 = ☐ %

h 14 out of 25 = ☐ %

i 9 out of 20 = ☐ %

Write these percentages as fractions.

j $20\% = \dfrac{☐}{5}$

k $90\% = \dfrac{☐}{10}$

l $75\% = \dfrac{☐}{4}$

m $60\% = \dfrac{☐}{5}$

n $25\% = \dfrac{☐}{4}$

o $12\% = \dfrac{☐}{25}$

p $45\% = \dfrac{☐}{20}$

q $98\% = \dfrac{☐}{50}$

II Calculate these.

a 20% of 80 cm = ☐ cm

b 10% of £2.50 = ☐ p

c 25% of 400 ml = ☐ ml

d 5% of 80 kg   = ☐ kg

e 20% of £12.50 = £ ☐

f 25% of 3.2 m = ☐ m

g 30% of 200 cm = ☐ cm

h 60% of 40 l   = ☐ l

Approximation and rounding

When you round to the nearest 10, 100 or 1000, the halfway position is important.

nearest 10:

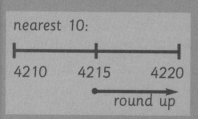

nearest 100:

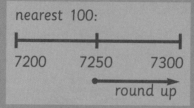

nearest 1000:

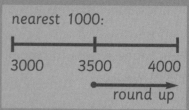

Numbers that are halfway or beyond are **rounded up**. The rest are **rounded down**.

I Round these numbers.

	to the nearest 10	to the nearest 100	to the nearest 1000
a 43 179 →			
b 789 155 →			
c 261 004 →			
d 749 968 →			
e 415 584 →			
f 29 465 →			
g 414 563 →			
h 254 564 →			

II Round these to work out approximate answers.

a

DAILY NEWS

The music festival had record crowds. 68,759 people went on Saturday, with 79,839 people on Sunday.

This is an approximate total of _____.

b

DAILY NEWS

The ancient woods were in a rectangular shape 978 metres long and 214 metres wide.

The approximate area of the woods is
_____ m².

c

DAILY NEWS

The shopping centre had 211,482 visitors last month and 294,182 visitors this month.

This is an increase of approximately
_____ visitors.

Equations

Equations have symbols or letters instead of numbers. You need to work out the missing numbers.

$x + 3 = 8$	$3n = 12$	$\frac{y}{2} = 8$
Use subtraction to help.	This means $n \times 3$.	This means $y \div 2$.
$8 - 3 = 5$ so $5 + 3 = 8$	Use division $12 \div 3 = 4$ so $3 \times 4 = 12$	Use multiplication $8 \times 2 = 16$ so $16 \div 2 = 8$
$x = 5$	$n = 4$	$y = 16$

 Work out the value of each letter.

a $4 + y = 9$

   $y = $ ☐

b $a - 5 = 7$

   $a = $ ☐

c $4c = 20$

   $c = $ ☐

d $x + 8 = 15$

   $x = $ ☐

e $\frac{x}{4} = 6$

   $x = $ ☐

f $12 - y = 8$

   $y = $ ☐

g $5n = 30$

   $n = $ ☐

h $18 + y = 30$

   $y = $ ☐

i $\frac{a}{6} = 3$

   $a = $ ☐

Work out the value of each letter. These are tricky, so show your working out.

a $2x + 4 = 10$

   $x = $ ☐

b $18 - 3y = 3$

   $y = $ ☐

c $5a - 15 = 10$

   $a = $ ☐

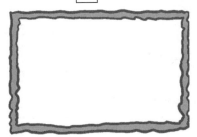

d $4c + 1 = 9$

   $c = $ ☐

e $3x - 5 = 13$

   $x = $ ☐

f $5 + 2a = 11$

   $a = $ ☐

Fractions of amounts

To find a fraction of an amount, divide by the denominator.

$\frac{1}{4}$ of 24 = 24 ÷ 4 = 6

$\frac{3}{4}$ ← numerator
    ← denominator

When the numerator is more than 1, divide by the denominator and multiply by the numerator:

$\frac{1}{4}$ of 24 = 6

$\frac{3}{4}$ of 24 = 6 × 3 = 18

I   **Answer these.**

a What is $\frac{3}{5}$ of:

40 → ⬜

25 → ⬜

15 → ⬜

100 → ⬜

b What is $\frac{3}{4}$ of:

20 → ⬜

12 → ⬜

40 → ⬜

100 → ⬜

c What is $\frac{2}{3}$ of:

21 → ⬜

9 → ⬜

18 → ⬜

33 → ⬜

d $\frac{7}{8}$ of 800 ml = ⬜ ml

e $\frac{2}{5}$ of 1000 g = ⬜ g

f $\frac{2}{3}$ of 90 cm = ⬜ cm

g $\frac{9}{10}$ of 70 kg = ⬜ kg

h $\frac{3}{8}$ of 72 km = ⬜ km

i $\frac{5}{6}$ of 180 l = ⬜ l

II   **Answer these.**

a What fraction of 1 year is 1 week? ⬜

b What fraction of 1 hour is 45 minutes? ⬜

c What fraction of 1 metre is 700 centimetres? ⬜

d What fraction of £8 is 25p? ⬜

e What fraction of 1 day is 8 hours? ⬜

f What fraction of 1 year is 4 weeks? ⬜

g What fraction of 1 minute is 20 seconds? ⬜

h What fraction of £12 is 50p? ⬜

26

Angles

Learn these rules for working out angles.

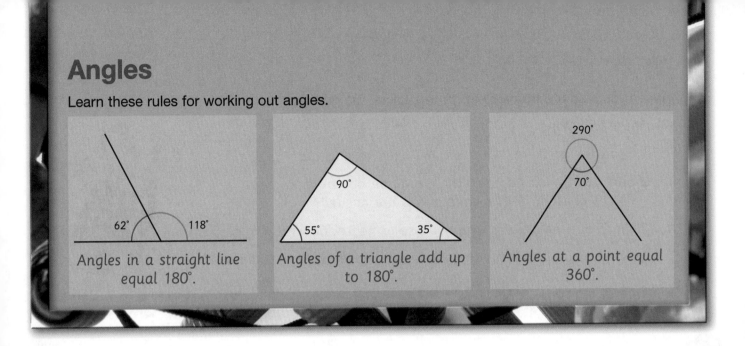

| Angles in a straight line equal 180°. | Angles of a triangle add up to 180°. | Angles at a point equal 360°. |

I Work out the size of the missing angles.

a

b

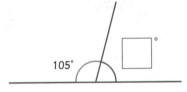

c

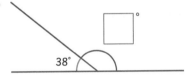

d

265°

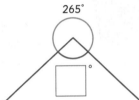

e

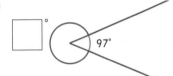

97°

f

250°

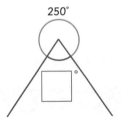

g

50°   38°

h

49°
85°

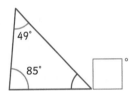

i

115°
26°

II Work out these missing angles.

a

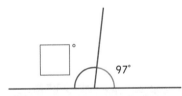

? ?
60° 40°   45° 50°

b

80°
100°
?
?

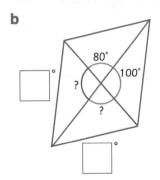

c

?
35°
46°   80°
?

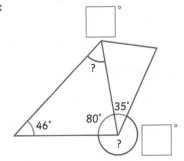

Word problems

When you read a word problem, try to 'picture' the problem.

Try these four steps.

1 Read the problem. What do you need to find out?

2 Sort out the calculation. There may be one or more parts to the question. What calculations are needed?

3 Work out the answer. Will you use a mental or written method?

4 Check back. Read the question again. Have you answered it fully?

I Answer these word problems.

| Grass seed £6.70 | Lawnmower £94.75 | Large pot £11.40 | Spade £9.23 | Hedge trimmer £107.59 | Fork £8.38 |

a What is the cost of a spade, a fork and some grass seed? _____

b How much change from £100 would there be if you bought a lawnmower? _____

c What is the cost of two pots and a hedge trimmer? _____

d What would be the total cost of five packets of grass seed? _____

What change would there be from £50? _____

e What is the difference in price between the spade and fork? _____

II Answer these questions about a trip to a fairground.

PRICES

| Dizzy Dipper £1.90 | X-ray Ride £2.05 | Super Spin £1.80 | Giant £2.15 | Mars Mission £1.35 | Big Wheel £1.55 |

Each of these children went on two rides. Which two rides did they go on?

a Alex: £1.50 change from £5. _____

b Harry: £6.30 change from £10. _____

c Rebecca: 15p change from £4. _____

d Emma: £5.95 change from £10. _____

e Which of these rides is the mean average price for the six rides? _____

Multiplication

There are different ways to work out multiplication calculations.

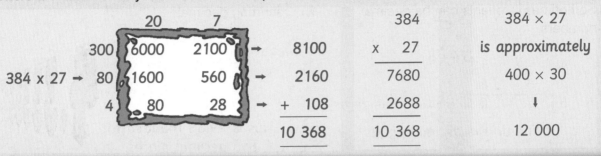

	20	7			384	384 × 27
300	6000	2100	→ 8100	x	27	is approximately
384 x 27 → 80	1600	560	→ 2160		7680	400 × 30
4	80	28	→ + 108		2688	↓
			10 368		10 368	12 000

I Answer these.

a 194 × 28

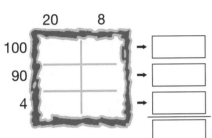

```
      20    8
100 [        ]  →  [      ]
 90 [        ]  →  [      ]
  4 [        ]  →  [      ]
                  [      ]
```

b 263 × 34

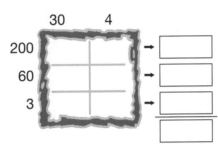

```
      30    4
200 [        ]  →  [      ]
 60 [        ]  →  [      ]
  3 [        ]  →  [      ]
                  [      ]
```

c 382 × 36

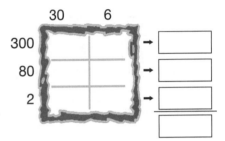

```
      30    6
300 [        ]  →  [      ]
 80 [        ]  →  [      ]
  2 [        ]  →  [      ]
                  [      ]
```

d
```
      235
×      31
_____

_____
_____
```

e
```
      419
×      28
_____

_____
_____
```

f
```
      327
×      43
_____

_____
_____
```

II The volume of a cuboid is length × width × height. Calculate the volume of these cuboids.

a
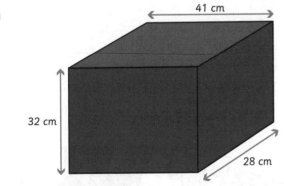

41 cm
32 cm
28 cm

Volume = _____ × _____ × _____

= [   ] cm³

b
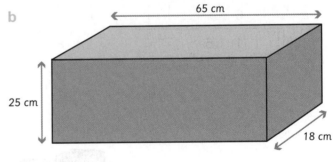

65 cm
25 cm
18 cm

Volume = _____ × _____ × _____

= [   ] cm³

Which cuboid has the greatest volume? _____

Division

A **quotient** is an answer to a division. Sometimes quotients can be decimal numbers.

Some decimal quotients go on and on as recurring decimals.

$$274 \div 5$$

```
    5 4 . 8
5 ⟌ 2 7 4 . 0 0   ← add some zeros
      2    ↑4
   line up the decimal points
```

$$238 \div 3$$

```
    7 9 . 3 3 3
3 ⟌ 2 3 8 . 0 0 0
      2   1 1 1
```

This is 79.33 rounded to two decimal places.

 Answer these using decimals.

a 5 ⟌ 1 4 7

c 2 ⟌ 7 4 7

e 8 ⟌ 3 2 5

g 4 ⟌ 6 4 9

b 4 ⟌ 2 1 5

d 5 ⟌ 4 1 8

f 2 ⟌ 8 9 7

h 8 ⟌ 4 7 1

Answer these, rounding the answer to two decimal places.

i 6 ⟌ 1 7 5

k 7 ⟌ 1 4 9

m 7 ⟌ 3 0 9

o 3 ⟌ 4 6 9

j 3 ⟌ 2 5 0

l 9 ⟌ 4 3 6

n 9 ⟌ 6 4 7

p 6 ⟌ 5 0 8

All the 2s and 3s are missing. There are four of each number. Write them in the correct places.

a
```
    6 ☐ . ☐
5 ⟌ ☐ 1 6
```

b
```
      7 ☐ . ☐ 5
8 ⟌ 5 8 6
```

c
```
      1 ☐ 0 . 5
4 ⟌ 5 ☐ ☐
```

Coordinates

Graphs have **axes**.

Axes are used to plot **coordinates**.

Position A is at (3, 2)

Position B is at (2, −4)

Position C is at (−2, 3)

Position D is at (−2, −2)

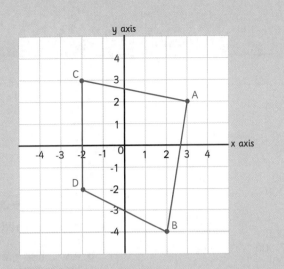

I **Draw these four triangles with the following coordinates.**

Triangle A

(2, 2) (4, 6) (7, 3)

Triangle B

(2, −2) (4, −6) (7, −3)

Triangle C

(−2, −2) (−4, −6) (−7, −3)

Triangle D

(−2, 2) (−4, 6) (−7, 3)

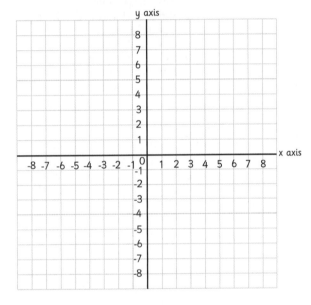

II **Plot these coordinates.**

(−4, 1)

(−8, 1)

(−5, 6)

(−1, 6)

Draw a reflection of this shape and write the coordinates.

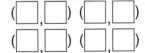

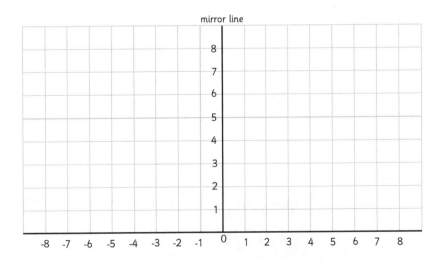

ANSWERS

Page 2

I a 74 500   **c** 48
561 000   273
865   49.1
29 800   621
311 400   380
2180   31.58
b 26 000   **d** 294
968 000   6148
6050   81.5
3   0.062
314 000   817
2 317 000   1722
19 800   13.1
1650   0.04

II a 100   **d** 6   **g** 100
b 0.57   **e** 1000   **h** 160.5
c 3.87   **f** 8500   **i** 94.13

Page 3

I a 23, 27, 31   Rule: +4
b −9, −17, −25   Rule: −8
c 13.5, 15, 16.5   Rule: +1.5
d 17, 50, 61
e 0.88, 0.87, 0.85
f 25, 10, −5
g 46, 55, 64
h 0.75, 1, 1.25
i −101, −82, −6

II a 25, 36, 49, 64
Rule: 1×1, 2×2, 3×3...etc.
They are square numbers.
b 15, 21, 28, 36
Rule: +2, +3, +4 etc
They are triangular numbers.
c 16, 32, 64, 128
Rule: Each number is double
the previous one.

Page 4

I a 3 tenths
b 6 thousandths
c 5 hundredths
d 8 tenths
e 6 hundredths
f 9 thousandths
g 1.99, 2.0
h 3.021, 3.022
i 4.95, 4.951
j 1.001, 1.002

II a 1.046   **c** 1.004
b 1.247   **d** 1.058

Page 5

I a 930, 2004, 825, 726
b 296, 4120, 2004
c 2004
d 825, 930
e

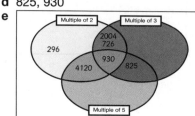

II a Tick boxes 2, 3, 4, 6, 7, 8, 9
b Check child's answer. Example
answers: 180, 360.
c 60

Page 6

I a 1:3
b 1:2
c 1:4
d a ➜16, b ➜24, c ➜12

II a Any 5 tiles red, any 15
tiles blue.
b Any 3 tiles green, any 12
tiles yellow.

Page 7

I a Quadrilateral, Square,
Rectangle, Rhombus,
Parallelogram, Trapezium, Kite
b Square, Rectangle, Rhombus,
Kite, Trapezium
c Square, Rectangle, Rhombus,
Parallelogram
d Square, Rhombus, Kite
e Square, Rectangle, Rhombus,
Parallelogram
f Square, Rectangle

II Check child's quadrilaterals.

Page 8

I a 6.05, 6.095, 6.198, 6.59,
6.625, 6.85, 6.9, 6.93
b 6.93   **c** 6.85   **d** 6.85
e Any of 6.05 6.095 6.198 6.59
or 6.625 **<6.82<** any of 6.85
6.9 or 6.93
f Any of 6.59 6.625 6.85 6.9 or
6.93 **>6.4>** any of 6.05 6.095
or 6.198
g Either 6.05 or 6.095 **<6.19<**
any of 6.198 6.59 6.625 6.85
6.9 6.93
II a Smallest – 1.269, 1.296, 1.629,
1.692, 1.926, 1.962
b Smallest – 9.126, 9.162, 9.216,
9.261, 9.612, 9.621

Page 9

I a

67	84	151
92	45	137
159	129	288

d

280	400	680
170	220	390
450	620	1070

b

108	29	137
176	52	128
184	81	265

e

450	120	570
370	260	630
820	380	1200

c

65	155	220
175	49	224
240	204	444

f

2600	3100	5700
1700	5800	7500
4300	8900	13200

g 16   **i** 55   **k** 500
h 38   **j** 565   **l** 5550

II a 18, 19, 20   **d** 167, 168, 169
b 26, 27, 28   **e** 31, 32, 33
c 112, 113, 114   **f** 90, 91, 92

Page 10

I a (1, 45) (3, 15) (5, 9)
b (1, 18) (2, 9) (3, 6)
c (1, 63) (3, 21) (7, 9)
d (1, 30) (2, 15) (3, 10) (5, 6)
e (1, 42) (2, 21) (3, 14) (6, 7)

f (1, 40) (2, 20) (4, 10) (5, 8)
g (1, 48) (2, 24) (3, 16) (4, 12) (6, 8)
h 1, 5, 25
i 1, 7, 49
j 1, 2, 4, 8, 64
k They have an odd number of
factors.

II

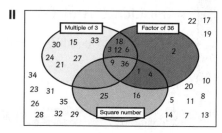

Page 11

I a 27, 27, 27   **d** 48, 48, 48
b 56, 56, 56   **e** 54, 54, 54
c 28, 28, 28   **f** 45, 45, 45

g

x	7	8	4
6	42	48	24
9	63	72	36
5	35	40	20

i

x	8	6	3
7	56	42	21
5	40	30	15
9	72	54	27

h

x	6	3	5
8	48	24	40
7	42	21	35
9	54	27	45

II a 8, 9, 6, 8, 7, 6
b 6, 9, 9, 10, 8, 3
c 9, 9, 9, 7, 4, 4
d 8, 7, 6, 6, 6, 7

Page 12

I a ÷2 = $\frac{3}{5}$ **f** ÷3 = $\frac{3}{8}$
b ÷4 = $\frac{1}{3}$ **g** $\frac{3}{5}$
c ÷5 = $\frac{2}{3}$ **h** $\frac{3}{5}$
d ÷4 = $\frac{5}{6}$ **i** $\frac{3}{4}$
e ÷10 = $\frac{3}{10}$

II

Page 13

I Estimates may vary slightly.
a estimate: 120   124.14
b estimate: 22   21.97
c estimate: 90   86.25
d estimate: 71   71.26
e estimate: 210   213.5
f estimate: 260   254.19
g estimate: 510   506.1
h estimate: 580   579.55

II Van A ➜ 80.59 kg + 85.17 kg +
34.24 kg
Van B ➜ 60.59 kg + 62.57 kg +
76.84 kg

Page 14

I
a 12.27 d 25 mins
b 1 hr 48 mins e Train 1
c 2 hrs 11 mins f 1 hr 4 mins

II Check your child's answer.

Page 15

I
a tetrahedron (triangular based pyramid)
b cuboid
c square based pyramid
d cube
e triangular prism
f pentagonal based pyramid

II cube: 6, 12, 8
cuboid: 6, 12, 8
tetrahedron: 4, 6, 4
square-based pyramid: 5, 8, 5
pentagonal prism: 7, 15, 10
triangular prism: 5, 9, 6

Page 16

I
a area = 52 m² perimeter = 34 m
b area = 130 m² perimeter = 56 m
c area = 116 m² perimeter = 52 m
d area = 70 m² perimeter = 44 m
e area = 72 m² perimeter = 46 m
f area = 43 m² perimeter = 28 m

II
a 27 m² c 175 m²
b 98 m² d 300 m²

Page 17

I
a 110, 110, 110, 94, 86, 86, 74, 70, 70
b 110 cm
c 86 cm
d 90 cm

II
a mode → 7
median → 7
mean → 7
b They are all the same.
c Check child's answer.

Page 18

I a

b

c

d

e

f

g

h

II
a b c

Page 19

I
a 44.19 km, 44 190 m
b 7
c 4.8 m
d 600.4 km

II
a Anty b Dennis

Page 20

I Check child has circled a, b, c, d and j.
Check child has coloured c and j.

II
a $\frac{1}{5}$ $\frac{3}{10}$ $\frac{1}{2}$ d $\frac{11}{20}$ $\frac{7}{10}$ $\frac{4}{5}$
b $\frac{7}{12}$ $\frac{2}{3}$ $\frac{3}{4}$ e $\frac{1}{4}$ $\frac{1}{3}$ $\frac{3}{8}$
c $\frac{2}{3}$ $\frac{5}{6}$ $\frac{11}{12}$ f $\frac{1}{4}$ $\frac{7}{12}$ $\frac{5}{6}$

Page 21

I a

b 5 litres e 9 litres
c 8 pints f 13.5 litres
d 5 pints g 5 gallons

II °C 25° 34° 80° 12° 42° 20° 30° 68°
°F 75° 90° 175° 50° 105° 65° 85° 150°

Page 22

I Estimate may vary slightly.
a estimate 8 7.92
b estimate 25 25.39
c estimate 47 46.74
d estimate 36 35.94
e estimate 141 141.78
f estimate 284 284.17
g estimate 443 442.7
h estimate 78 77.66

II
a 3 3 1 . 6 9
  − 5 8 . 7 4
  2 7 2 . 9 5

b 2 7 1 . 9
  − 1 0 6 . 7 1
  1 6 5 . 1 9

c 1 0 6 . 9
  − 8 8 . 7
  1 8 . 2

d 4 6 4 . 8 2
  − 2 1 5 . 7
  2 4 9 . 1 2

Page 23

I
a 60% g 60% m 3
b 75% h 56% n 1
c 90% i 45% o 3
d 84% j 1 p 9
e 20% k 9 q 49
f 96% l 3

II
a 16 cm d 4 kg g 60 cm
b 25p e £2.50 h 24 l
c 100 ml f 0.8 m

Page 24

I
a 43180, 43 200, 43 000
b 789 160, 789 200, 789 000
c 261 000, 261 000, 261 000
d 749 970 , 750 000, 750 000
e 415 580, 415 600, 416 000
f 29 470, 29 500, 29 000
g 414 560, 414 600, 415 000
h 254 560, 254 600, 255 000

II Approximations may vary slightly.
a 150 000 c 80 000 visitors
b 200 000 m²

Page 25

I a 5 d 7 g 6

b 12 e 24 h 12
c 5 f 4 i 18

II
a 3 c 5 e 6
b 5 d 2 f 3

Page 26

I
a 24, 15, 9, 60 f 60 cm
b 15, 9, 30, 75 g 63 kg
c 14, 6, 12, 22 h 27 km
d 700 ml i 150 l
e 400 g

II
a $\frac{1}{52}$ d $\frac{1}{32}$ g $\frac{1}{3}$
b $\frac{3}{4}$ e $\frac{1}{3}$ h $\frac{1}{24}$
c $\frac{7}{10}$ f $\frac{1}{13}$

Page 27

I
a 75° d 95° g 92°
b 142° e 263° h 46°
c 83° f 110° i 39°

II
a 80°, 95°, 85°
b 100°, 80°
c 54°, 245°

Page 28

I
a £24.31 d £33.50, £16.50
b £5.25 e 85p
c £130.39

II
a Giant and Mars Mission
b Dizzy Dipper and Super Spin or Big Wheel and Giant
c X-ray Ride and Super Spin
d Dizzy Dipper and Giant
e Super Spin

Page 29

I
a 5432 c 13 752 e 11 732
b 8942 d 7285 f 14 061

II
a 36 736 cm³ b 29 250 cm³
a has the greatest volume

Page 30

I
a 29.4 g 162.25 m 44.14
b 53.75 h 58.875 n 71.89
c 373.5 i 29.17 o 156.33
d 83.6 j 83.33 p 84.67
e 40.625 k 21.29
f 448.5 l 48.44

II
a   6 3 . 2
  5 ⟌ 3 1 6

b   7 3 . 2 5
  8 ⟌ 5 8 6

c   1 3 0 . 5
  4 ⟌ 5 2 2

Page 31

I

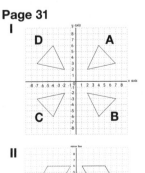

II

(4,1) (8,1) (5,6) (1,6)

Test 1 Multiply and divide by 10, 100 and 1000

When **multiplying by 10, 100** or **1000** move the digits the correct number of places **to the left**.

When **dividing by 10, 100** or **1000** move the digits the correct number of places **to the right**.

Write the missing numbers.

1. 36   ×   ⬚   =   36000

2. 4.21   ×   100   =   ⬚

3. ⬚   ÷   10   =   78.5

4. 0.9   ×   ⬚   =   9

5. 1603   ÷   100   =   ⬚

6. ⬚   ÷   100   =   451

7. 1000   ×   ⬚   =   6338000

8. 9720   ÷   ⬚   =   97.2

9. 340   ÷   1000   =   ⬚

10. ⬚   ×   100   =   201

Colour in your score

Test 1

Test 2 Division facts

Use **multiplication facts** to help work out **division facts**.

Answer these.

1. 81 ÷ 9 =

2. 56 ÷ 7 =

3. 28 ÷ 4 =

4. 42 ÷ 6 =

5. 27 ÷ 3 =

6. 24 ÷ 8 =

7. 35 ÷ 7 =

8. 54 ÷ 9 =

9. 32 ÷ 8 =

10. 48 ÷ 6 =

Colour in your score

Test 2

Test 3 Problems

£68.75   £9.99   £11.86   £22.50

Write the answers to these problems.

1. What is the cost of 4 CD's?

2. How much change would there be from £100 if you bought the CD player?

3. What is the difference in price between the CD holder and the headphones?

4. What is the total cost of the CD player, the headphones and the CD holder?

5. How much change would there be from £50 if you bought 3 CD's?

6. 42cm is cut off a length of wood 4.5m long. The rest is cut into 6 equal lengths. What is the length of each piece?

7. If a glass holds 280ml and 4 glasses are filled from a 2 litre bottle full of milk, how much milk is left?

8. Cinema tickets for an adult cost £4.35 and £2.96 for a child. A family ticket for 2 adults and 2 children costs £12.00. How much is saved by buying a family ticket?

9. David is 33cm taller than his sister. She is half the height of their father, who is 178cm tall. How tall is David?

10. 3 parcels weigh a total of 2kg. 2 of the parcels weigh the same amount and the other is half the weight of one of the other parcels. What is the weight of each parcel?

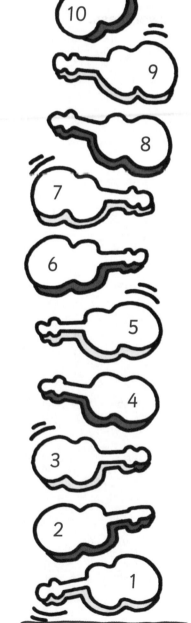

Colour in your score

Test 3

Test 4 Fractions

To **order fractions**, change them so they all have the **same denominator**.

$$\frac{15}{20} = \frac{3}{4}$$

Simplify these fractions.

1. $\frac{20}{25}$ = ☐

2. $\frac{14}{21}$ = ☐

3. $\frac{18}{24}$ = ☐

4. $\frac{9}{15}$ = ☐

5. $\frac{20}{24}$ = ☐

Write these fractions in order starting with the smallest.

6. $\frac{1}{2}$ $\frac{5}{6}$ $\frac{3}{4}$ $\frac{7}{8}$ ☐ ☐ ☐ ☐

7. $\frac{10}{20}$ $\frac{6}{20}$ $\frac{14}{20}$ $\frac{15}{20}$ ☐ ☐ ☐ ☐

8. $\frac{3}{6}$ $\frac{12}{18}$ $\frac{5}{6}$ $\frac{4}{18}$ ☐ ☐ ☐ ☐

9. $\frac{15}{20}$ $\frac{4}{20}$ $\frac{10}{20}$ $\frac{6}{20}$ ☐ ☐ ☐ ☐

10. $\frac{25}{40}$ $\frac{20}{40}$ $\frac{10}{40}$ $\frac{16}{40}$ ☐ ☐ ☐ ☐

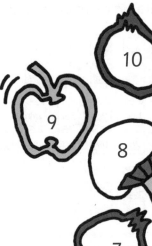

10
9
8
7
6
5
4
3
2
1

Colour in your score

Test 4

Test 5 Ratio and proportion

Ratio is used to **compare 2 quantities**.

Proportion is the **fraction of the whole**.

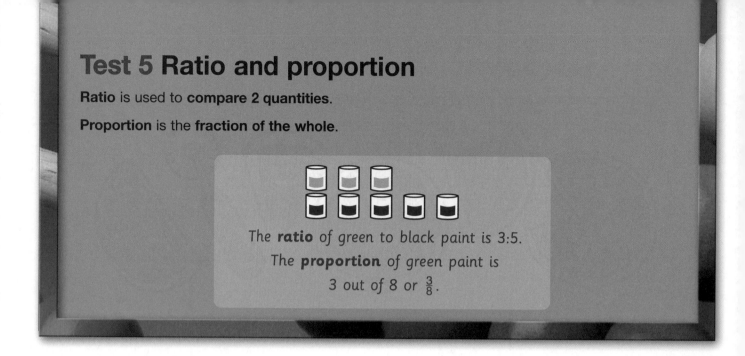

The **ratio** of green to black paint is 3:5.
The **proportion** of green paint is
3 out of 8 or $\frac{3}{8}$.

Write the ratios of green paint to black paint.

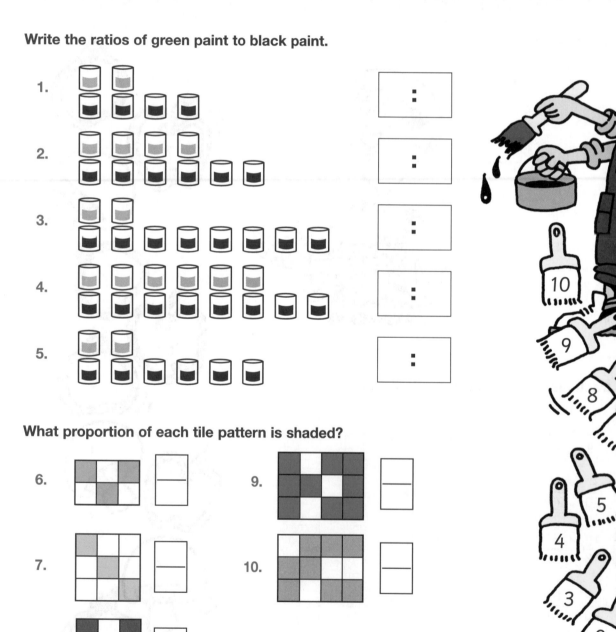

1. [:]

2. [:]

3. [:]

4. [:]

5. [:]

What proportion of each tile pattern is shaded?

6.

7.

8.

9.

10.

Colour in your score

Test 5

Test 6 Averages

Mean, mode and **median** are all different types of **averages**.

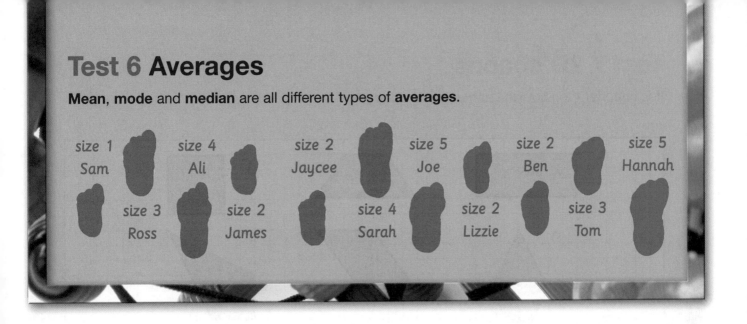

size 1 Sam   size 4 Ali   size 2 Jaycee   size 5 Joe   size 2 Ben   size 5 Hannah

size 3 Ross   size 2 James   size 4 Sarah   size 2 Lizzie   size 3 Tom

Write the answers to these problems.

1. Write the shoe sizes in order starting with the smallest.

2. What is the mean size of all the children?

3. What is the median size?

4. What is the mode size?

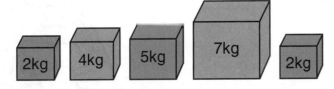

2kg   4kg   5kg   7kg   2kg

5. What is the median weight of the boxes?

6. What is the mode weight?

7. What is the mean weight of all the boxes?

34   29   27   32   27   34   27

8. What is the mean of these numbers?

9. What is the mode?

10. What is the median?

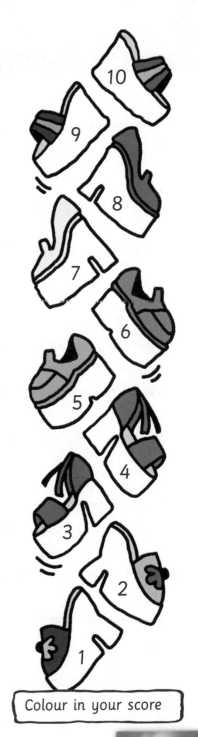

10
9
8
7
6
5
4
3
2
1

Colour in your score

Test 6

Test 7 2D shapes

It is important to know the names of **2D shapes**.

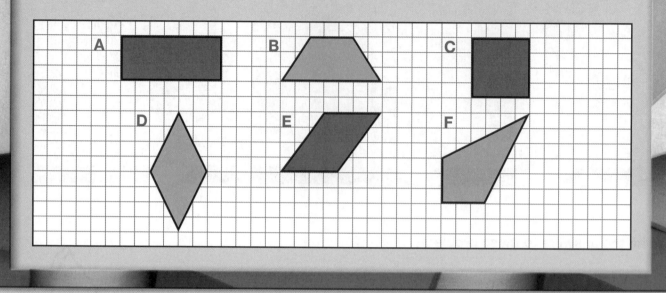

Write the answers to these questions.

1. Which shape is a parallelogram?

2. What is the name of shape A?

3. Which shape is a square?

4. What is the name of shape F?

5. Which shape is a rhombus?

6. What is the name of shape B?

7. What are all of these shapes called?

8. Which shape has 4 right angles and
   4 equal sides?

Draw lines of symmetry on each shape.

9.

10.

Colour in your score

Test 7

Test 8 Measures

Pints and **gallons** are **imperial** units of measure; **litres** are **metric** units of measure. These graphs convert between different units.

gallons to litres

litres

25 —
20 —
15 —
10 —
5 —
0 —

0 1 2 3 4 5
gallons

litres to pints

pints 10 —
8 —
6 —
4 —
2 —
0 —

0 1 2 3 4 5 6
litres

Use the conversion graphs above to write the missing measures.

(≈ means approximately equal to.)

1. [ ] litres ≈ 2 gallons

2. 7 pints ≈ [ ] litres

3. [ ] pints ≈ 1.2 litres

4. [ ] gallons ≈ 22.5 litres

5. 2 litres ≈ [ ] pints

6. [ ] litres ≈ 0.5 gallons

7. [ ] gallons ≈ 13.5 litres

8. 1.75 pints ≈ [ ] litres

9. [ ] pints ≈ 4.5 litres

10. [ ] litres ≈ 3 gallons

Colour in your score

Test 8

Test 9 Addition and subtraction (1)

Use **mental methods** to add and subtract.

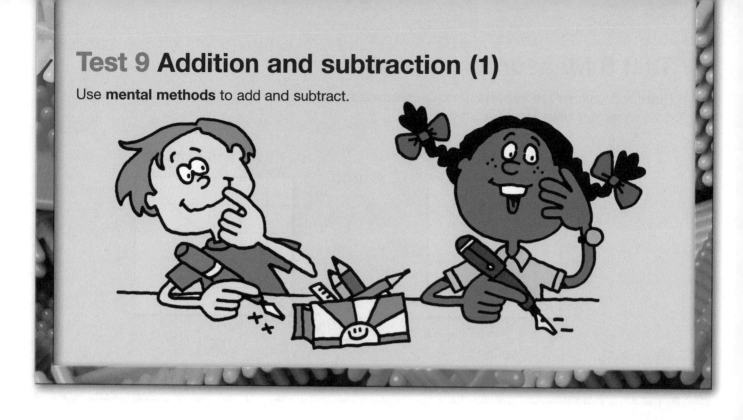

Write the answers.

1. 63 + 84 =

2. 127 – 98 =

3. 209 + 155 =

4. 4300 – 2600 =

5. 712 – 330 =

6. 960 + 450 =

7. 307 + 88 =

8. 149 – 79 =

9. 6320 – 1800 =

10. 2900 + 4700 =

Colour in your score

Test 9

Test 10 Patterns and sequences

Looking at differences between **numbers in a sequence** can show the pattern or rule.

Continue these sequences.

1. | 27 | 19 | 11 | 3 | −5 | | |

2. | −9 | 3 | 15 | 27 | 39 | | |

3. | 4.5 | 7 | 9.5 | 12 | 14.5 | | |

4. | 1 | 2 | 4 | 7 | 11 | | |

5. | 128 | 64 | 32 | 16 | 8 | | |

Write the missing numbers in these sequences.

6. | −1 | −5 | | | −17 | −21 |

7. | 1.5 | | | 2.25 | 2.5 | 2.75 |

8. | | | 37 | 43 | 49 | 55 |

9. | | 17 | | −13 | −28 | −43 |

10. | 5 | | 11 | | 25 | 35 |

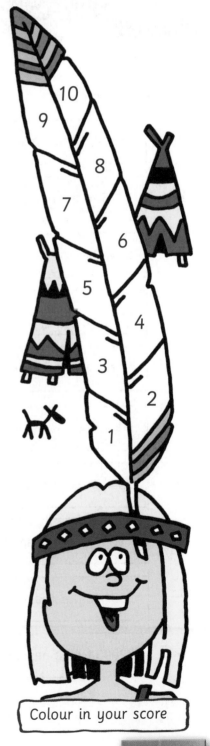

Colour in your score

Test 10

Test 11 Approximation and rounding

When you **round** to the nearest 10, 100 or 1000, the **halfway position** is important. **Halfway** points are always rounded up.

Round these numbers.

1. 35604 to the nearest 10

2. 7955 to the nearest 100

3. 81428 to the nearest 1000

4. 2365 to the nearest 10

5. 177912 to the nearest 1000

6. 900648 to the nearest 100

7. 39524 to the nearest 1000

8. 11870 to the nearest 100

9. 7651 to the nearest 10

10. 22098 to the nearest 1000

Colour in your score

Test 11

Test 12 Multiplying decimals

Estimate first to check an answer.

Answer these.

1.	4.5	×	7	=	
2.	3.8	×	6	=	
3.	1.29	×	3	=	
4.	0.07	×	9	=	
5.	6.4	×	8	=	
6.	5.13	×	5	=	
7.	9.78	×	4	=	
8.	7.03	×	8	=	
9.	6.25	×	7	=	
10.	4.48	×	9	=	

Colour in your score

Test 12

Test 13 Number problems (1)

Read the questions carefully and work out the calculations you need.

Write the answers to these questions.

1. How much heavier is 5.19kg than 3.73kg?

2. What is 5.39cm add 7.06cm?

3. A jug holds 500ml of drink. If 87.5ml is poured out, how much drink is left in the bottle?

4. Kate has £86.42. She has £27.29 more than Hannah. How much money does Hannah have?

5. If you bought 2 items for £66.74 and £92.85, how much change would you get from £200?

6. A piece of wood was cut into 8 equal lengths, each measuring 9.6cm. How long was the piece of wood before it was cut?

7. What is the total cost of £14.57, £26.92 and £18.65?

8. What is the difference in weight between 400g and 133.5g?

9. A car travels 42.7km on Monday, 39.6km on Tuesday, 54.9km on Wednesday, 27.5km on Thursday and 48.3km on Friday. What is the total distance travelled?

10. The same car travelled 127.8km on Saturday and 96.5km on Sunday. How much further did the car travel in total at the weekend than during the week?

Colour in your score

Test 13

Test 14 Fractions and quantities

To find $\frac{2}{3}$ of £24:

- find $\frac{1}{3}$ of £24 = £8
- then $\frac{2}{3}$ is £8 x 2 = £16

$\frac{2}{3}$ of £24 is £16

Write the answers to each of these problems.

1. What is three quarters of 80?

2. What fraction of 1 hour is 40 minutes?

3. $\frac{4}{5}$ of 65cm =

4. Find $\frac{7}{8}$ of 400g.

5. What fraction of 2m is 60cm?

6. What is $\frac{2}{5}$ of 700km?

7. Find $\frac{6}{7}$ of 56.

8. $\frac{3}{100}$ of 600ml =

9. What is $\frac{5}{6}$ of 360?

10. What fraction of £12 is 50p?

Colour in your score

Test 14

Test 15 Coordinates

Axes are used to plot **coordinates** on **graphs**.

Plot these positions on the graph.

1. Position A is at (2, 6).

2. Position B is at (-1, 7).

3. Position C is at (5, 6).

4. Position D is at (-2, -7).

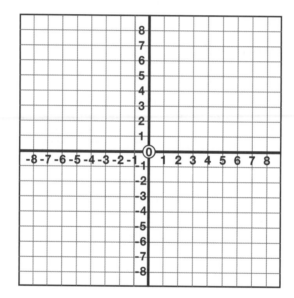

Draw these triangles.

5. Triangle K
   (4, 4) (4, -3) (2, -3)

6. Triangle L
   (-3, 5) (-6, 2) (-1, 1)

7. Triangle M
   (-3, -1) (-6, -4) (-3, -6)

Plot these positions on the graph.

8. Plot the following
   coordinates: (-4, 6)
   (0, 3) (-4, 1) (-6, 4).
   Join them in order.

9. Draw a reflection of
   the shape.

10. Write the coordinates
    of this shape.

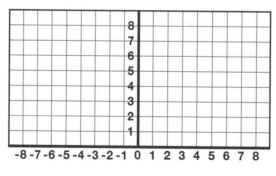

(_ , _) (_ , _) (_ , _) (_ , _)

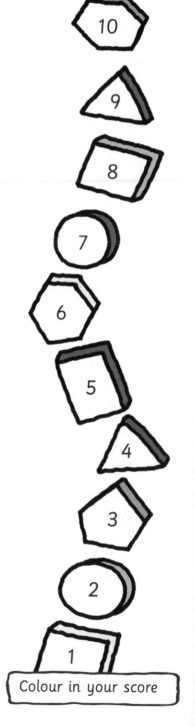

Colour in your score

Test 15

Test 16 Data handling

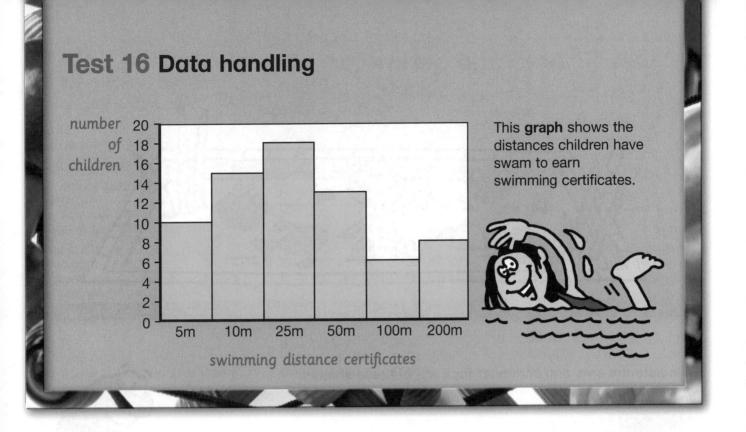

number of children

This **graph** shows the distances children have swam to earn swimming certificates.

swimming distance certificates

Write the answers.

1. How many children got 100m certificates?

2. How many children got 10m certificates?

3. How many children can swim further than 50m?

4. How many more children got 25m certificates than 5m?

5. Which distance had 13 certificates?

6. Which distance had 2 more certificates than the 100m distance?

7. What distance did the least number of children achieve?

8. How many children received certificates?

9. What was the total distance covered by children who achieved 5m certificates?

10. What was the total distance covered by children who achieved 50m certificates?

10
9
8
7
6
5
4
3
2
1

Colour in your score

Test 17 Area and perimeter

The **area** of rectangles = length × width.

The **perimeter** is the distance all the way round.

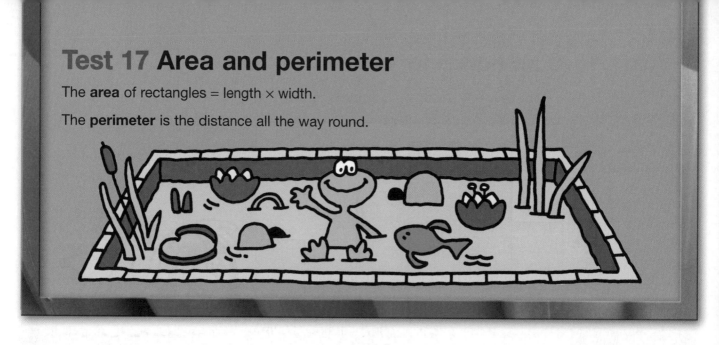

Calculate the area and perimeter for each of these shapes.

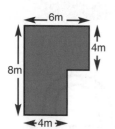

1. area = ☐ m²

2. perimeter = ☐ m

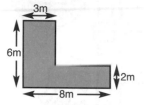

3. area = ☐ m²

4. perimeter = ☐ m

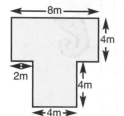

5. area = ☐ m²

6. perimeter = ☐ m

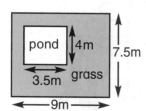

7. What is the area of the pond? ☐ m²

8. What is the perimeter of the pond? ☐ m

9. What is the area of the whole garden? ☐ m²

10. What is the area of the grass? ☐ m²

Colour in your score

Test 17

Test 18 Addition and subtraction (2)

Estimate the answer to the nearest whole number first and then calculate.

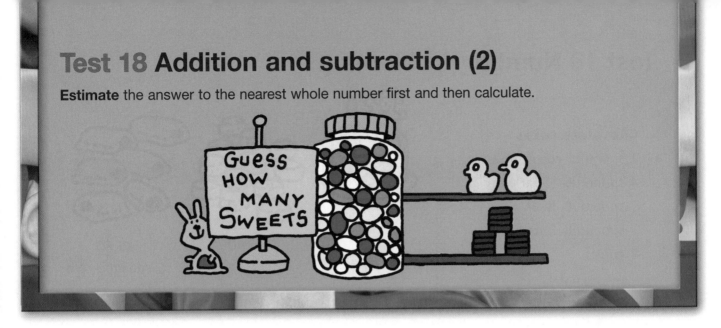

Write the approximate answer to the nearest whole number.
Write the actual answers.

8.9 + 6.2

1. Approx :

2. Actual :

4.3 + 9.6

3. Approx :

4. Actual :

7.7 + 8.8

5. Approx :

6. Actual :

4.2 + 9.8

7. Approx :

8. Actual :

3.9 + 7.5

9. Approx :

10. Actual :

10
9
8
7
6
5
4
3
2
1

Colour in your score

Test 18

Test 19 Number problems (2)

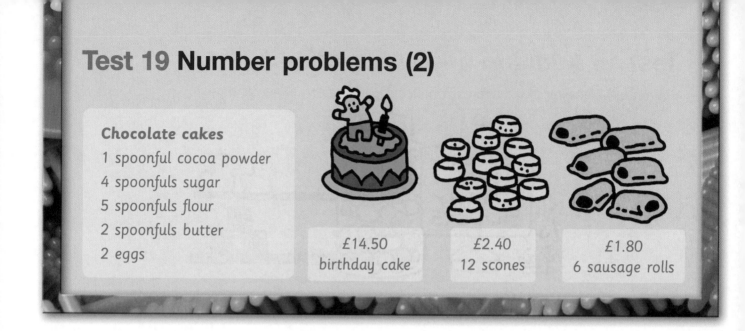

Chocolate cakes

1 spoonful cocoa powder

4 spoonfuls sugar

5 spoonfuls flour

2 spoonfuls butter

2 eggs

£14.50
birthday cake

£2.40
12 scones

£1.80
6 sausage rolls

Use the recipe above to answer these problems.

1. If 1 spoonful is 25g and 1 egg is 30g, how much cake mixture will be made using this recipe?

2. How many 45g cakes can be made from this recipe?

3. If 15 spoonfuls of flour are used, how many spoonfuls of butter will be needed?

4. If 16 spoonfuls of sugar are used, how many eggs will be needed?

5. The cakes take 25 minutes to cook. If they are put in the oven at 5.48 pm, what time will they be ready?

Use the prices above to answer these problems.

6. How much more does 1 sausage roll cost than 1 scone?

7. What change would you have from £20 if you bought a birthday cake, a pack of scones and a pack of sausage rolls?

8. The packs of scones are on offer, 'Buy 2 get 1 free'. How much would it cost for 9 packs?

9. Birthday cakes are reduced by 20%. What is the new price?

10. There are 36 guests at a birthday party. What is the total cost for 1 birthday cake and enough packs of sausage rolls and scones for the guests to have 1 of each?

Colour in your score

Test 19

Test 20 Properties of numbers

Numbers all have different properties.

9

9 is a square number (3^2)
9 is a multiple of 3 (3×3)
9 is an odd number

Which of these numbers is:

63	50	81	23

1. a square number?

2. a multiple of 7?

3. an even number?

4. a prime number?

Which of these numbers is:

24	17	27	15	64	14

5. a factor of 60?

6. a multiple of 6?

7. a factor of 56?

8. a multiple of 9?

9. a square number and a multiple of 8?

10. an odd number and a factor of 34?

Colour in your score

Test 20

Test 21 Decimals (1)

The **decimal point** separates **units** from **tenths**.

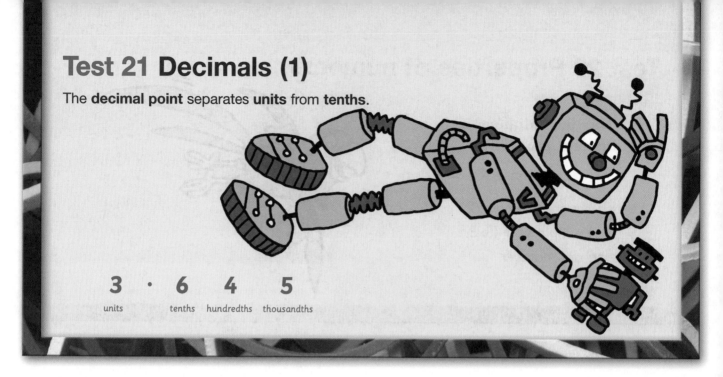

3 · 6 4 5

units · tenths hundredths thousandths

Write the value of the bold digit.

1. 42.13**5** ⟹

2. 8.0**9** ⟹

3. 12.7**2**6 ⟹

4. 390.**5**48 ⟹

5. 41.60**7** ⟹

6. 7.9**5** ⟹

Make a decimal number as near as possible to 5.

(There must be one number in front of the decimal point.)

7. 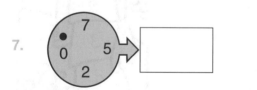 ⟹

9. 4 • 5 9 0 ⟹

8. 9 3 1 • 4 ⟹

10. 2 6 7 1 • ⟹

Test 22 Multiplication

It is sometimes better to use a **written method** for multiplying large numbers.

Calculate the answer for each of these.

1.
```
    2 5 3
  ×   1 7
  _____
```

6.
```
    1 6 7
  ×   2 1
  _____
```

2.
```
    4 9 6
  ×   3 2
  _____
```

7.
```
    2 8 5
  ×   2 5
  _____
```

3.
```
    8 0 4
  ×   2 4
  _____
```

8.
```
    3 1 9
  ×   4 7
  _____
```

4.
```
    1 1 5
  ×   4 6
  _____
```

9.
```
    7 0 4
  ×   3 5
  _____
```

5.
```
    3 2 9
  ×   1 8
  _____
```

10.
```
    5 6 8
  ×   3 3
  _____
```

Colour in your score

Test 23 Division

Use a **written method** to work out division using large numbers.

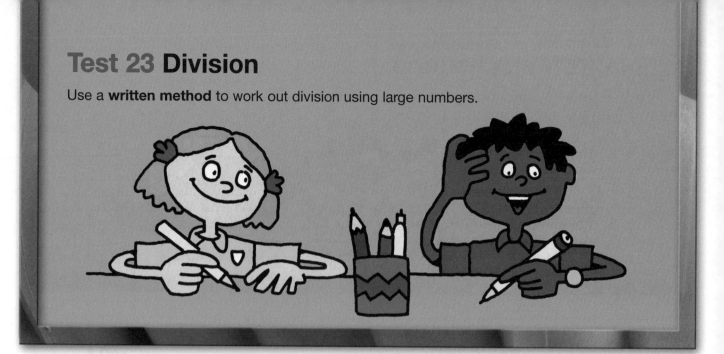

Answer these.

1. 14 ⟌ 7 8 4

2. 27 ⟌ 9 4 5

3. 35 ⟌ 6 3 0

4. 18 ⟌ 4 3 2

5. 33 ⟌ 9 5 7

6. 19 ⟌ 5 8 9

7. 26 ⟌ 4 4 2

8. 32 ⟌ 4 1 6

9. 21 ⟌ 8 8 2

10. 16 ⟌ 6 2 4

Colour in your score

Test 23

Test 24 Decimals (2)

To **order decimals**, line them up with the decimal point aligned.

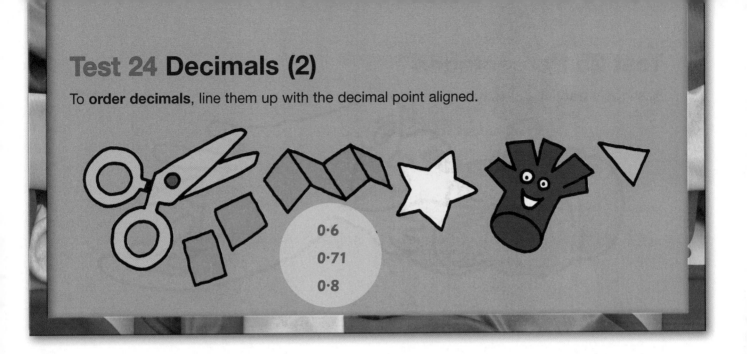

0·6

0·71

0·8

Write these numbers in order, starting with the smallest.

1. 0·9   0·09   0·89

2. 0·32   0·23   0·03

3. 0·04   0·6   0·464

4. 0·517   0·52   0·702

Write the decimal number these arrows point to.

5. [ ]   6. [ ]   7. [ ]

0   0.01

Use these 4 cards to make:

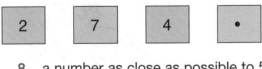

8. a number as close as possible to 5.

9. a number as close as possible to 3.

10. a number as close as possible to 4.

Colour in your score

Test 24

Test 25 Percentages

% shows a **fraction** out of **100**.

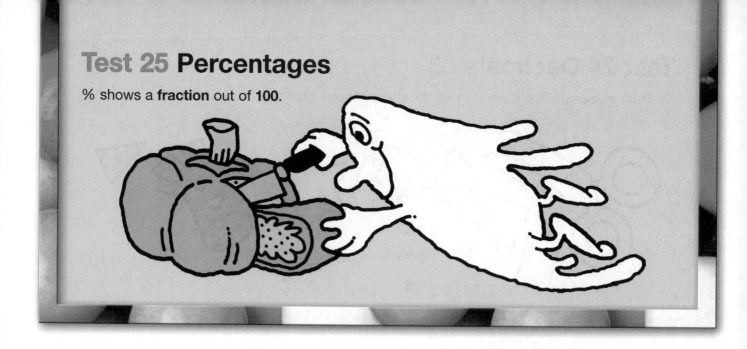

Write these fractions as percentages.

1. $\dfrac{3}{10}$ = [ ]

2. $\dfrac{7}{20}$ = [ ]

3. $\dfrac{4}{25}$ = [ ]

4. $\dfrac{2}{5}$ = [ ]

Write these amounts.

5. 30% of 200ml = ⟹ [ ]

6. 10% of 400kg = ⟹ [ ]

7. 80% of 100cm = ⟹ [ ]

8. 5% of 80g = ⟹ [ ]

9. 25% of 400m = ⟹ [ ]

10. 15% of 60l = ⟹ [ ]

Colour in your score

Test 26 Data

This graph shows the number of bananas and apples sold in the school tuck shop over a term.

_____ apples

················ bananas

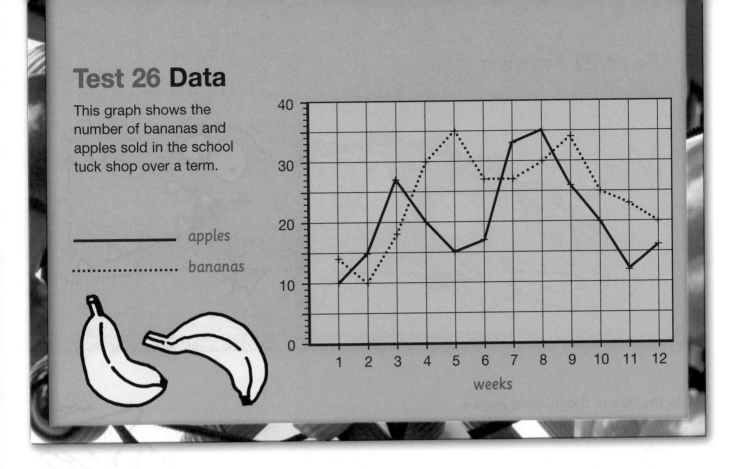

weeks

Answer the following questions.

1. How many bananas were sold in week 8?

2. In which week were most apples sold?

3. In which week were 23 bananas sold?

4. How many more bananas were sold in week 5 than apples?

5. How many apples were sold in week 12?

6. In which week were the fewest apples sold?

7. What is the difference between the numbers of bananas sold in week 4 and week 5?

8. Which weeks were more apples sold than bananas?

9. In which week was the most fruit (bananas and apples) sold?

10. How many apples were sold in total this term?

Colour in your score

Test 26

Test 27 Angles

It is important to remember the rules about **angles**.

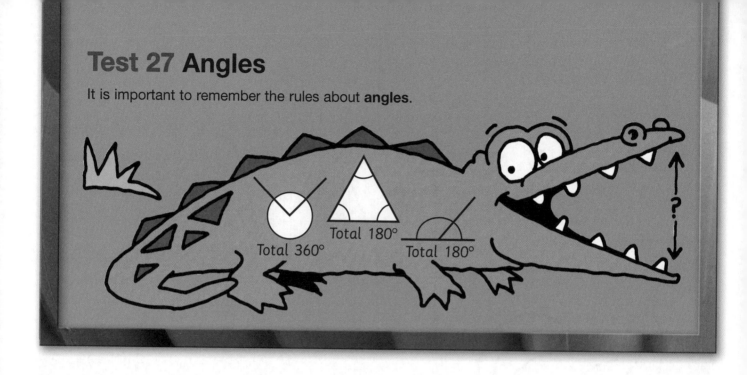

Total 360° Total 180° Total 180°

Write the size of the missing angles.

1. 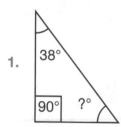 38° 90° ?° ☐

6. 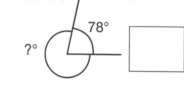 78° ?° ☐

2. ?° 40° 56° ☐

7. ?° 297° ☐

3. ?° 74° 59° ☐

8. ?° 25° 49° ☐

4. 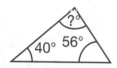 ?° 35° ☐

9.  208° 78° ?° ☐

5. 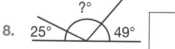 ?° 136° ☐

10. 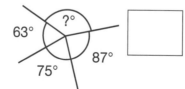 63° ?° 75° 87° ☐

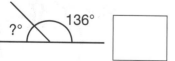

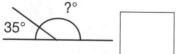

Colour in your score

Test 27

Test 28 Time

am → before midday

pm → after midday

The 24-hour clock uses 4 digits.

Write these times using am and pm.

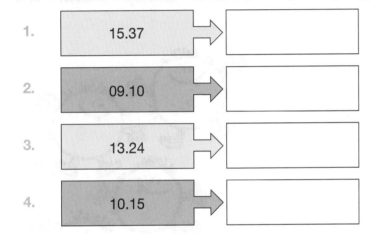

1. 15.37

2. 09.10

3. 13.24

4. 10.15

Write these times using the 24-hour clock.

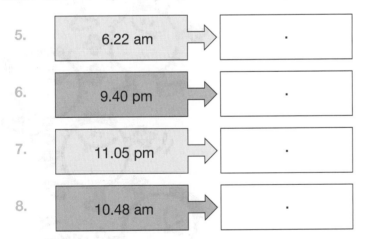

5. 6.22 am   .

6. 9.40 pm   .

7. 11.05 pm   .

8. 10.48 am   .

Write these times 25 minutes earlier.

9. 16.13

10.

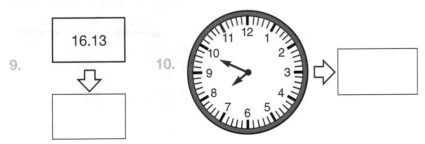

Colour in your score

Test 28

Test 29 Addition and subtraction (3)

When adding and subtracting **decimal numbers**, make sure the decimal points all line up.

Answer these.

1.
```
    2 5 . 6 2
     9 . 7 0
  + 4 3 1 . 0 8
  _____
```

2.
```
    6 0 . 2 4
  + 3 9 8 . 9 7
  _____
```

3.
```
    1 3 2 . 7 5
  -  4 4 . 9 0
  _____
```

4.
```
    2 5 1 . 1 0
  -   1 7 . 3 6
  _____
```

Use a written method to answer these.

5. 24.5 + 138.74 + 6.09 =

6. 251.92 − 64.83 =

7. 48.66 + 193.78 =

8. 102.23 − 15.97 =

9. 684.7 + 35.62 =

10. 127.5 − 46.88 =

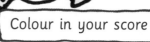

Colour in your score

Test 29

Test 30 Equations

Equations have **symbols** or **letters** instead of numbers.

Work out the value of each letter.

1. $7 + x = 15$

   $x = \boxed{}$

2. $18 - y = 11$

   $y = \boxed{}$

3. $\dfrac{a}{4} = 3$

   $a = \boxed{}$

4. $5b = 30$

   $b = \boxed{}$

5. $12 - 2c = 2$

   $c = \boxed{}$

6. $3x - 9 = 15$

   $x = \boxed{}$

7. $4y + 3 = 11$

   $y = \boxed{}$

8. $7 + 2a = 23$

   $a = \boxed{}$

9. $5x - 10 = 20$

   $x = \boxed{}$

10. $26 - 4y = 14$

    $y = \boxed{}$

Colour in your score

ANSWERS

Test 1
1. 1000
2. 421
3. 785
4. 10
5. 16·03
6. 45100
7. 6338
8. 100
9. 0·34
10. 2·01

Test 2
1. 9
2. 8
3. 7
4. 7
5. 9
6. 3
7. 5
8. 6
9. 4
10. 8

Test 3
1. £39.96
2. £31.25
3. £10.64
4. £103.11
5. £20.03
6. 68cm
7. 880ml
8. £2.62
9. 122cm
10. 400g, 800g, 800g

Test 4
1. $\frac{4}{5}$
2. $\frac{2}{3}$
3. $\frac{3}{4}$
4. $\frac{3}{5}$
5. $\frac{5}{6}$
6. $\frac{1}{2}$ $\frac{3}{4}$ $\frac{5}{6}$ $\frac{7}{8}$
7. $\frac{6}{20}$ $\frac{10}{20}$ $\frac{14}{20}$ $\frac{15}{20}$
8. $\frac{4}{18}$ $\frac{3}{6}$ $\frac{12}{18}$ $\frac{5}{6}$
9. $\frac{4}{20}$ $\frac{6}{20}$ $\frac{10}{20}$ $\frac{15}{20}$
10. $\frac{10}{40}$ $\frac{16}{40}$ $\frac{20}{40}$ $\frac{25}{40}$

Test 5
1. 1:2
2. 2:3
3. 1:4
4. 3:4
5. 1:3
6. $\frac{1}{2}$ or $\frac{3}{6}$
7. $\frac{1}{3}$ or $\frac{3}{9}$
8. $\frac{4}{9}$
9. $\frac{3}{4}$ or $\frac{9}{12}$
10. $\frac{2}{3}$ or $\frac{8}{12}$

Test 6
1. 1, 2, 2, 2, 2, 3, 3, 4, 4, 5, 5
2. 3
3. 3
4. 2
5. 4kg
6. 2kg
7. 4kg
8. 30
9. 27
10. 29

Test 7
1. E
2. rectangle
3. C
4. kite
5. D
6. trapezium
7. quadrilaterals
8. square
9.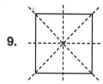
10.

Test 8
(answers are approximate)
1. 9 litres
2. 4 litres
3. 2 pints
4. 5 gallons
5. 3·5 pints
6. 2·25 litres
7. 3 gallons
8. 1 litre
9. 8 pints
10. 13·5 litres

Test 9
1. 147
2. 29
3. 364
4. 1700
5. 382
6. 1410
7. 395
8. 70
9. 4520
10. 7600

Test 10
1. -13, -21
2. 51, 63
3. 17, 19.5
4. 16, 22
5. 4, 2
6. -9, -13
7. 1·75, 2
8. 25, 31
9. 32, 2
10. 7, 17

Test 11
1. 35600
2. 8000
3. 81000
4. 2370
5. 178000
6. 900600
7. 40000
8. 11900
9. 7650
10. 22000

Test 12
1. 31·5
2. 22·8
3. 3·87
4. 0·63
5. 51·2
6. 25·65
7. 39·12
8. 56·24
9. 43·75
10. 40·32

Test 13
1. 1·46kg
2. 12·45cm
3. 412·5ml
4. £59.13
5. £40.41
6. 76.8cm
7. £60.14
8. 266.5g
9. 213km
10. 11.3km

Test 14
1. 60
2. $\frac{2}{3}$ or $\frac{40}{60}$
3. 52cm
4. 350g
5. $\frac{3}{10}$ or $\frac{60}{200}$
6. 280km
7. 48
8. 18ml
9. 300
10. $\frac{1}{24}$

Test 15

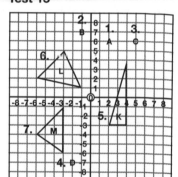

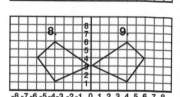

10. (4,6) (0,3) (4,1) (6,4)